The Man's Eyes
Followed the Woman.

Observation was engrained in his nature, and a part of his mind noted that her legs were shaven to a glossy smoothness. It was a fact, and he dealt in facts. But the more primitive part of him noted that those legs would be silky to the touch.

He lifted his gaze to encounter cool, haughty eyes. Set in a sculpted face, the ebony-fringed eyes were as pale gray as the here-and-there sagebrush that salted the landscape, and just as tenacious and unyielding. He knew at once that this was the Widow Woman whose name had been on the tip of every tongue.

And he knew at once that he wanted the Widow Woman.

W0010270

Dear Reader:

There is an electricity between two people in love that makes everything they do magic, larger than life. This is what we bring you in SILHOUETTE INTIMATE MOMENTS.

SILHOUETTE INTIMATE MOMENTS are longer, more sensuous romance novels filled with adventure, suspense, glamor or melodrama. These books have an element no one else has tapped: excitement.

We are proud to present the very best romance has to offer from the very best romance writers. In the coming months look for some of your favorite authors such as Elizabeth Lowell, Nora Roberts, Erin St. Claire and Brooke Hastings.

SILHOUETTE INTIMATE MOMENTS are for the woman who wants more than she has ever had before. These books are for you.

Karen Solem
Editor-in-Chief
Silhouette Books

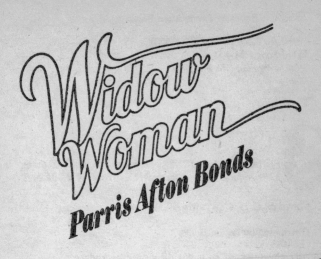

Widow Woman

Parris Afton Bonds

Silhouette Intimate Moments
Published by Silhouette Books New York
America's Publisher of Contemporary Romance

Silhouette Books by Parris Afton Bonds

Made for Each Other (ROM #70)
Wind Song (IM #5)
Widow Woman (IM #41)

SILHOUETTE BOOKS, a Division of Simon & Schuster, Inc.
1230 Avenue of the Americas, New York, N.Y. 10020

ISBN: 0-671-47131-7

First Silhouette Books printing March, 1984

10 9 8 7 6 5 4 3 2 1

America's Publisher of Contemporary Romance

Printed in the U.S.A.

*For Linda and Robert Cudd,
and in memory of Thomas Thompson.*

With special thanks to Chief John Lewis of the Eddy County Sheriff's Department and Captain Conn Brown of the New Mexico State Police.

Chapter 1

HE CROSSED HIS ARMS AND LAZED AGAINST THE old Mercury station wagon parked next to the rural mailbox. Above the hard, high cheekbones his eyes were slitted against the April sun's early morning light. His watchful gaze followed the silhouettes of the jogger and the dog that loped alongside. They were the solitary figures on the isolated stretch of desert basin that was cradled by the miragelike Pyramid and Burro mountain ranges, ragged tailends of the Rockies trailing down to the boot heel of New Mexico. Mysterious Hidalgo County, with its mining ghost towns, was New Mexico's least explored part—and the last place one would expect to see a jogger.

The jogger's shoes kicked up little puffs of

dust on the caliche road that intersected the two-lane highway. Straight and rigid as a gun barrel and smelling rankly of hot tar, the highway bisected vast, empty Hidalgo County near where it bordered Mexico. As the dog and the jogger, moving in lithe, easy strides, neared the intersection and the lone man, their pace slowed to a wary walk. Across the width of the highway the two people regarded each other. The large dog that looked like a cross between a coyote and a German Shepherd growled softly, until the jogger placed a restraining hand on its head.

The man's eyes followed the long length of the woman's slender tanned legs upward. Observation was engrained in his nature, and a peripheral part of his mind noted that the well-shaped legs were shaven to a glossy smoothness. It was a fact, nothing more, and he dealt in facts. But a more primitive part of him noted that those legs would be silky to the touch.

His assessing gaze tarried on her expensive white terry running shorts before sliding on up to the powder pink tee shirt. It was stenciled with the words *Woman Power*. Sweat soaked a splotch between the high, firm breasts that reminded him of rounded pomegranates, ripe for eating.

He dragged his gaze away to encounter cool, haughty eyes. Set in a sculpted face, the ebony-fringed eyes were as pale gray as the here-and-there sagebrush that salted the landscape, and just as tenacious and unyielding. He knew at once that this was the Widow Woman, whose name had been on the tip of every tongue back in Lordsburg.

And he knew at once that he wanted the Widow Woman.

He left the highway shoulder's slag of broken stone, glass shards and flattened beer cans and crossed to her. In that empty county of less than five thousand people she should perhaps have been afraid of the powerfully built man with the Hispanic bow nose who approached her, but if she was, she gave no indication of it.

He took his time as he ambled across, hands jammed in his faded jeans pockets. He chalked up a point in her favor for the way she held her ground, meeting his eyes. She shook her head, flicking back the long, damp strands of her summer-child's white hair that had escaped her top knot and clung to her neck. A studier of people and their habits, he knew then that she was slightly uneasy.

He came to stand before her and the dog, whose hackles bristled. The man was of average height, and the woman was taller than most, so her direct gaze was on a level with his. He was surprised that those sage-gray eyes, so vivid beneath straight dark brows, were devoid of makeup. The striking face, covered with a sheen of perspiration, was as fresh as the new day. He repressed the sudden urge to take her shoulders and . . .

"He wanted to know where the turnoff was to Reinhart Farms," Cassie told her father as she tossed the mail and the morning's paper she had collected on the entryway's Mexican chest. "A *campesino*, no doubt."

But it was early in the season, by almost two weeks, for the migrant farm workers to hit the chile, cotton, and pinto bean fields of the truck farms. And there had been something about the man that did not quite fit her conception of the common laborer. The broad shoulders had been far from stooped, and the proud, oblique face hadn't worn the hang-dog expression so characteristic of the Mexican-Americans, blacks and poor whites who made the migrant circuit.

Ben Duval, who had imparted his height to his daughter, strapped on a Colt single action .357 magnum. The pearl handle, studded with turquoise, he had made himself as a young man when he had homesteaded the one-hundred-and-sixty-acre ranch with his bride. "You should cut the jogging, Cassie. More and more jobless people taking to the roads all the time. Too dangerous to be out wandering around alone. Take the pickup to get the mail."

Cassie eyed the lean, weathered man with the fierce mustachioed face in amusement. "Pee Wee was with me. Besides, I jogged every day in Manhattan and was never attacked once."

The drooping white mustache twitched in annoyance. "Course not. All fags up there in Cement City." He pinned the Hidalgo County Sheriff's badge to his plaid flannel shirt. "Never could figure out how you could stand living there all these years. Reckon the high pay held you there after Mario died."

Cassie's throat sealed over tighter than a tomb. She turned away and strode toward the kitchen. The copper pots she rattled in preparation for Davey's breakfast didn't drown out her father's gruff yet tender voice. He followed her to collect the battered Stetson from its peg near the side door. "My grandson needs a father. He's almost five. You oughta settle down. Too many years hopscotching across the globe have made you forget what a home is. What you need is a man."

She slapped a slab of bacon into the cast-iron skillet. "That's why I came back—so Davey and I could settle down. But we don't need a man to do that."

Ben tugged the hat over his thick iron-gray hair with a shake of his head. "Widow Woman! Bah!"

Long after her father had gone, Cassie stood at the sink, looking through the dust-filmed window at the emptiness that stretched beyond the ranchhouse's surrounding chaparral of mesquites and cottonwoods until the burning bacon and Davey's sleepy call of "Mama" reminded her that the long nine-year night-mare was over.

Nine-thirty and already the sun was merciless. The only sounds in that hot, oxygen-starved air were the beat of her shoes against the sun-baked earth, Pee Wee's soft panting and the furious but even pounding of her blood in her ears. Two months in New Mexico still had not reaccustomed her to the altitude of the high desert. In Manhattan she had run four miles a day to keep her model's figure. Now, by the time she jogged the two miles to the mailbox at the intersection of Highway 338, she was as tired as a chile picker and usually wound up walking the two-mile trip back to the ranchhouse.

Normally when she jogged she willed her mind to be a blank, as she had often done when she had to sit for long hours beneath the hot lights. But today thoughts intruded. Davey's asthma had become better with the move to the high, dry climate. She hoped that there would be no more injections for her son.

She was right to have retired when she had, at the peak of her career. In that profession one rarely succeeded past twenty-five, and she was twenty-seven.

Twenty-seven years old and already she had had enough of the fast life to last her through two lifetimes.

Ten years earlier she had been eager to escape the isolation of ranch life and its hard, rough work for the prestigious Juilliard School of Music and the bright city lights of New York. But her scholarship had dropped by the wayside at her meeting with the brilliant Italian composer and songwriter, Mario Garolini.

Eager, impetuous, innocent, naive . . . and unwise. Yet time had taught her much. Never would she return to that make-believe world. Reality was here at the ranch—hers and Davey's refuge. Here they were safe from scandalmongers, who would destroy the normal life she meant for Davey to live. She would fight to prevent any invasion of her privacy, should she have to.

Through the shimmering heat rising off the powdery earth her vision focused on the parked car at the intersection ahead and the lone figure propped against it. The man from yesterday. He uncrossed his feet—he wore scuffed, dark suede shoes, she remembered—and slowly strode toward her. Her rhythmic steps faltered and lagged, and she walked the remainder of the intervening distance. It was better to show no hesitation or indecision; that much she had learned from her dealings with the paparazzi, who, like bloodhounds, could smell a story in the making.

She was panting as heavily as Pee Wee. Perspiration rolled down the valley between her breasts, and she stifled the need to wipe it away with the hem of her tee shirt. At the highway's shoulder she drew abreast of him.

He was as darkly tanned as an Hispanic or an Indian, and his features were as fierce and proud. Despite the fact that she was almost as tall as he, there was a solidness about his build that created a Goliath effect and left the indelible impression of power restrained.

She had planned to ignore him and collect the mail, but something in his face halted her steps. The yellowish hazel eyes glittered warmly while the lips, deeply carved and generous, tossed her a raffish smile.

She nodded impersonally and resumed her walk across the highway to the mailbox. Her eyes flicked a contemptuous glance at the dilapidated station wagon parked a few feet away. As she leafed through the mail she felt his gaze moving leisurely over the backs of her legs and her shorts-clad derriere. A slow heat followed in the wake of the path his gaze burned.

An envelope from the Davison Agency. She hoped that it was a late commission check. The checks were dwindling now.

She turned around. She was right. He *was* watching her. He stood on the far side of the highway, feet planted apart, hands braced on hips, in a stance that announced arrogant assurance. She drew a deep breath and started back across the highway. As she drew near, Pee Wee began that soft growl. "Easy, Pee Wee," she murmured.

When she would have passed the man by, Pee Wee halted and bared his fangs—the usual reaction, and she should have expected it—but not now, not when she wanted only to ignore the stranger. The man dropped to one knee and held out a large, capable hand. "Careful, you'll lose some fingers," she said tonelessly, resenting even the few words she was forced to speak.

The stranger spoke softly in Spanish to the dog. She remembered some of the words from childhood, when she had played with the few Mexican American children who had been able to come to school. Most, even the six-year-olds, had worked the fields whenever they could.

At the man's murmured *"Dulce . . . dulce,"* Pee Wee dropped down on all fours at the man's knee and docilely permitted the stranger to stroke his furry throat. Cassie's mouth dropped open, but she quickly recovered her aplomb when the man rose from his haunches to face her again. "Part coyote?" he asked, his voice sounding like soft thunder to her.

She nodded.

"The wild ones, when they're tamed, always make the best companions."

She disregarded the innuendo behind the statement. She wanted only to move on, to get away from the magnetism the man seemed to wield. A diesel truck shot by, buffeting the two of them with hot wind. The stranger reached out to brush back the damp hair that the wind had whipped across her face. At her feet Pee Wee whined warningly, but the man didn't retract his hand. Instead his fingers tucked the stray strands behind her ear.

Her breath became clogged deep in her throat, as if she had asthma instead of Davey. It had been so long since she had known a man's nearness. Or had she ever? Those years of marriage didn't count.

The way the man looked at her—did he recognize her? From the skin medication ads in the teen magazines? Hardly. And not likely either from her foreign cover layouts. Few migrants could even read, much less peruse such a magazine. There were the myriad television commercials, but that had been years earlier, before her price had skyrocketed and her fame had made her name, Cass, a household word—first in Mario's native Italy, then throughout the rest of Europe, before she had finally captivated the western hemisphere. The man could have caught one of the few talk shows she had done in the United States. But then again, how many migrant workers owned televisions?

Respecting her desire for anonymity, her father had never boasted of his daughter's career to the people of Lordsburg. To them she was simply the Duval girl who had gone off to a New York college, married some prominent foreigner and come back a widow. After all, who would identify the plump little girl that they had known with Cass, the stunning model? Perhaps that was why, rather than try to pronounce the difficult name of Garolini, the Lordsburg community simply referred to her as the Widow Woman.

Without removing his hand, the man broke the spell. "I'm looking for a job."

"Try the growers." Her voice seemed little more than a rasp.

He shook his head, and a swath of leather-brown hair drifted across his forehead. "Hun-uh."

"Are you on the run from *La Migra*?" she asked suspiciously, referring to the Department of Immigration and Naturalization's Border Patrol.

"No." His fingers, rough with calluses, brushed the length of her neck before dropping to hitch in his belt loop. "I just want part-time work."

Released, she stepped back a pace, her flesh still tingling where his fingers had been. She knew that her father's horse ranch could use an extra hand. Even with everything she did, it wasn't enough. In the two months since her return to Lordsburg to help her father, she had been appalled by the condition of the ranch. Weather rusted the corral gates and time eroded the barns and stalls.

Repairs alone could keep the man busy for months to come. But with the hard times, the sheriff's job barely paid the taxes and kept the place going. They couldn't even afford to hire a *mojado*, a wetback or illegal Mexican national, as some growers like Reinhart often did, to avoid the wage scale of the migrants.

"Land poor," her father would complain when he tugged off his boots late at night.

She shook her head, shaking off the hold the man seemed to have on her. "We don't need any help."

His hand caressed the dog's neck, and she trembled, as if she could actually feel that hand on her neck again, caressing, stroking. The trembling was merely the cooling-off effect after her sauna-hot run, she told herself. Her chest rose and fell with her shallow but labored breathing, drawing his gaze once more to her full breasts. Uneasy, she swung away.

"You better try one of the big cities like El Paso or Albuquerque if you want part-time work," she tossed over her shoulder.

Migrants—all of a kind. Always moving. Possessed by the wanderlust. Not her. She had exorcised the wanderlust of her childhood during all those years as a reigning international model. She recalled the many mornings when she would awaken, unable to remember for a moment either the hotel or the city in which she was staying. She thought of the assignments in glittering cities like Rome and Paris and against mystical backdrops like Cairo and Bombay. But there had been no permanent home for her or Davey. Nor a man.

Now she was home again. And a man—she had had a man. Her father provided what paternal image her son required. Yes, she much preferred to stay the Widow Woman.

Davey gave a whoop of laughter as his mother forked the bale of hay over the edge of the loft. The bale bounced below them and tumbled to the edge of one of the barn's open galvanized doors. His laughter turned to spasms of coughing that brought tears to his dark, innocent eyes and bent his little body double.

Cassie dropped to one knee and removed her work glove so she could push back her son's rumpled butternut curls. "It's the hay and dust, Davey. Go on back to the house for a while and watch television. The cartoons will be on soon."

Still coughing, the boy shook his head. "No way. I wanna help you."

She sighed. He was as stubborn as she. If she hadn't been so adamant about leaving the ranch life, if she had stayed and married one of the growers' sons . . . But then she wouldn't have had Davey. She gave him a loving swat on the behind. "Go on with you, Davey. I'll be in shortly, and we'll run into Lordsburg for an ice cream soda."

"Wow! Promise?"

"I promise." Anxiously she watched her son descend the wooden ladder. It was a long drop from the loft, and she wanted to help him. But he would have made a moue with his cupid's-

bow lips and uttered an exasperated, "Mama!
I can do it myself."

Had her mother ever been that protective?
She couldn't remember. The first day when
Cassie, barely six years old, rode the school
bus home her father had been waiting at the
intersection of Highway 338 to tell her that
her mother was dead. "Female's disease," he
had muttered, his face an ashen gray, his
hands shaking as he shifted the pickup's gear
into second.

The words had meant nothing to Cassie
then. But the aftereffects meant that she was
doing the cooking, cleaning and farm chores
of a grown woman. In her father's spare time
he had helped her with the chores and tried to
pamper her in other ways—taking her with
him in the summer on his daily tour of the
county's ranches, farms and campgrounds;
giving her music lessons, which he could ill
afford; buying her sweets, which were the last
thing her adolescent's rounded body needed,
at Cantu's old grocery store.

She was still doing those chores—but this
time because she wanted to. The New Mexico
air was clear, free of the urban pollution that
aggravated her son's asthma. And the ranch
represented security, a way of life untainted
by an aberrant society.

She wiped her hand on her jeans and slid
her glove back on, but when she turned back
to the waiting bales a man's voice called out to
her. Startled, she spun about and almost top-

pled over the edge of the loft. Blindly she flailed for the nearest support post. Steadied, she opened her eyes and looked down into the smoky gaze of the man she had met on the highway. Sunlight fanned through the doorway to illuminate him like some dark angel.

"What do you want?" she rapped out, her heart still thudding after her near fall.

Hands on hips, he tilted his head back and grinned. "A job."

"I told you, we don't need any—"

She broke off as he started toward the ladder. A wayward vagrant . . . no one here to help her . . . he could kill her . . . no one would ever know he had done it. Terrified, she tried to yell and couldn't.

He grasped the ladder's lowest rung and broke it away. "I'd say you do, Widow Woman." He tossed the rung on the hay-strewn ground and continued on up the ladder.

He knew who she was. Had he been asking questions about her? Frightened even more by the revelation, she swooped up the pitchfork. She aimed it at his midsection as he came up over the side of the hayloft and calmly approached her. "Get out—whoever you are!"

"I'm Cade Montoya."

She poked the pitchfork's tines against his stomach in warning. Solid, a wall of muscle, it didn't give. "My father's the—"

"Sheriff Duval." He eased the pitchfork

from her locked fingers, and she was too startled to resist. "And if he runs a check on me, as I'm sure he eventually will, he'll find that I'm an ex-convict."

The breath whooshed from her. An ex-con! She should scream, jump from the loft, anything but stand there locked in the sizzling heat of his gaze. He propped an arm on the pitchfork's handle. The workshirt's sleeves had been rolled up to expose his bronzed forearms. Striated with muscles, they were shadowed with the same crisp hair that matted his chest above the V-neck of his shirt. His face, not really a handsome face, but stamped with a rugged virility, had been casually shaved that morning. She noted that a groove dimpled his chin, as if God had put His finger there. Or Satan, more likely.

"Apart from that unsavory record," the man said candidly, and with a self-mockery that surprised her, "I am a very reliable and tireless hand."

Below, Pee Wee trotted into the barn. Cassie breathed a little easier. With a brave gesture she shoved the cotton-white curtain of her hair back over her shoulder, where it swayed against the small of her back. "Even if we needed help, we don't have the money to pay you."

His eyes glowed golden in the barn's dimness. With calculated deliberation they browsed over the sweat-sheened cleavage that showed above the baby-blue gingham shirt she had left unbuttoned low against the barn's heat. "I only want room and board."

Pee Wee yelped. The beast was no good to her down there. "We don't have any spare rooms." And if we did, we wouldn't give one to an ex-convict, she thought.

He shrugged. "You might change your mind." Then he surprised her even more by passing the pitchfork back to her. "Folks in Lordsburg tell me the Spring Chile Festival is next week. Reckon you'll be going. Save me a dance."

His presumption galled her. She shoved her way past him toward the ladder. "I don't dance. But even if I did, I wouldn't dance with you."

Chapter 2

SHE DIDN'T DANCE. HER MARRIAGE—MARIO—
had destroyed all the beauty music had held
for her. She associated music with Mario
sitting before the piano, the music notebook
he used to write in untouched. The whiskey
glass on the piano—touched too often.

Perhaps that was why she had turned to the
impersonality of the camera to help support
their extravagant life-style. Her modeling career had soared as his musical career had
dipped and drifted into oblivion. His drinking,
his inability to summon the Muses, had eaten
away at their marriage like a hideous leprosy.

Leaning against the old Steinway, she
picked out middle C. It sounded loud in the
empty house. Davey was out at the paddock

watching the newborn filly her father had helped foal late the night before.

"You never play anymore."

Cassie turned to find her father standing in the doorway. He jammed his Stetson on the old hat tree and eased his lanky body into the overstuffed chair that had been recovered almost as many times as Davey had had birthdays. "You know, your mother set quite a store by that piano. How she scrimped to see you'd get lessons."

Guiltily Cassie closed the lid and brushed her hands against each other, feeling the dust that coated the piano top. Never enough time to get everything done. No wonder her father had needed her help at the ranch. "I know how much Mother encouraged my music, Pa. And I know you scrimped to continue those lessons. But I just don't seem to have the desire to play anymore."

Ben leaned forward, drawing out the foil pouch of tobacco flakes from his shirt pocket. "What happened to kill that desire, daughter? In all this time you've been back you've never told me what doused the light that used to shine in your eyes. You were a child of the land . . . a fey . . . unfettered as the wild mustangs. . . . Now . . . now, I don't understand anything anymore. Getting too old, I guess." He nodded his head uncertainly. His veined hand trembled when he shook the flakes into the cornhusk paper and rolled himself a cigarette.

To tell her father about those years of her marriage would only bring him further pain. She went over and sat on the arm of the chair, laying her cheek atop his graying head. "Let's go into town for an ice cream soda, Pa. Like we used to."

"I thought you gave up sweets when you went off to college," he charged with a mischievous light in his rheumy eyes.

She had. Now she always kept fruit in a wooden bowl on the kitchen table, a habit she had formed in New York. "I promised Davey." She pinched the leathery cheek. "Besides, you'll enjoy it. Admit it."

He chuckled. "You always did have a way of getting around me, Cassie Duval. All right, all right, I give in. Let go of me, gal."

He rose slowly to his feet, adding, "Need to go into Lordsburg anyway. I want to check out a meeting that's going on at the old VFW hall. Some agitator here to stir up trouble with the migrants."

She had shopped in Lordsburg several times since her return, but few people recognized the stunning woman as the girl who had been awkward and round with baby fat. However, as people greeted her father on the sidewalk that evening, she could see in their eyes the surprise, followed by the sudden association their minds made, and at last the recognition.

"This isn't plump little Cassie Duval, is it?" she heard more than once. Davey, who knew his mother only as slim and beautiful, flicked her a look that said that these people were clearly from outer space.

When she entered the VFW hall with her father and Davey, it was her turn to be surprised. She should have known. She stood at the back of the bare room, listening to him speak. Cade Montoya. The agitator.

It was the same man she had left in the loft that morning. And yet it wasn't the same man. Oh, he wore the same time-softened workshirt and jeans. And he used the same colloquial speech as before, but his intelligence and sensitivity were evident as he quietly spoke.

He used simple words to address the motley gathering seated in the hall, and he avoided philosophizing in favor of clear illustration. Yet she sensed the powerful, volatile personality behind the words. As he talked in majestic cadences that entranced the ear he was at times beautiful, like a dark seraph.

Because of her striking features and coloring and svelte figure, she was accustomed to being stared at, whispered about. But this once she stood unnoticed. Even Davey, who was usually restless after more than a minute of inaction, seemed entranced by the resonant voice that flowed in some symphonic rhythm unknown to ordinary men.

"By uniting, you can demand to be treated better," the man told the farm workers. "You can demand the minimum wage. You can demand workers' compensation and disability insurance."

Among the sea of straw hats and many-colored scarves, a few shouts of approval interrupted the stranger, but he continued. "If you unite in striking, you can demand chemical toilets in the fields and electricity and sewers in the labor camps. Don't you realize that the growers are against your uniting? That by pitting one group of poor people against another—blacks against whites, Mexican nationals against Mexican-Americans—they divide and weaken you?"

A bearlike man two rows in front of Cassie sprang to his feet and waved a hamhock fist at Cade Montoya. "I know that only this will settle the problem," he said in heavily accented English. "Any green-card-carrying Mexes take my job, I will show them my fist."

"And the growers?" Cade pointedly asked from behind the podium.

"Robles!" Ben Duval said to Cassie in exasperation. "He's been a real troublemaker over the years. Always drunk, punching—"

Robles whipped out a knife, a switchblade. "I will show the growers this."

Gasps burst from those nearest the man. "Violence only settles the problem temporarily," Cade said softly as he walked with apparent confidence toward the man.

Though Cade was shorter than Robles, he gave the impression of being centered in himself so that no energy was wasted, an impression of density at the same time as he walked as lightly as a fox. She felt that this was a man who didn't stumble, and that to get to where he was going he would walk all day if necessary.

Cassie's father had already started down the aisle and he reached Robles first. With his pearl-handled .357 he prodded the man in the back. "Switchblades are illegal, Robles. You oughtta know better." He reached around the burly man and took the knife.

"See!" Robles spat at Cade. The florid Mexican-American sniffed through his nose, like a boxer. "Do you think *la chota* will help us? The law—it doesn't give a damn about the farm worker!"

"Come on, Robles," her father said. "Let's spend the night in *el tanque*."

"Is jailing necessary, Sheriff?" Cade asked. "Now that you have the knife, I think the danger is over."

Ben eyed Cade for a moment, as if trying to evaluate the man within. "A night in the tank will keep Robles from going home and beating his wife. Do you have a home, Montoya?"

Cade's smile was humorous as it met Cassie's. "No. Nor do I have a wife to beat."

"There's such a thing as a vagrancy charge," her father warned, but Cassie knew that he had already made up his mind in favor of Cade. Obviously he had yet to check Santa Fe's computer bank of criminal records.

"I'm staying with Armadeo for the time

being," Cade said, indicating the slight man
with only one arm who stood next to him.
Cassie knew Armadeo from school. He had
lost his arm the summer of second grade,
when he was working the cotton fields and
hadn't moved quickly enough from the path
of the tractor's harrow. Now he was the father
of seven children, four of whom worked in the
fields.

It was a never-ending cycle, and on the
return trip to the ranch Cassie pondered the
hopelessness of the farm workers' lives and
wondered why and how Cade Montoya had
become mixed up in the struggle for farm
workers' rights. Was he a union goon? She
doubted it. Where had he done time? Most
likely La Tuna, a federal prison near El Paso,
since it both incarcerated criminals and
served as a detention center for Mexican
nationals—wetbacks—being returned across
the border.

And what had he done time for? she asked
herself for the umpteenth time.

She pulled the sleeping Davey into the crook
of her arms and looked over at her father. He
also seemed preoccupied as he drove the
county's four-wheel-drive vehicle back to the
ranch. Every once in a while the voice of
the dispatcher would crackle across the two-
way radio, and she knew, out of the habit of
years, that her father was peripherally moni-
toring the mobile unit's calls.

"Pa, do you know anything about the man who spoke tonight, this Cade Montoya?"

His hooded eyes flicked her a glance. "He's not the settling-down type, Cassie."

She blushed in the darkness of the four-wheeler. "He doesn't interest me that way, Pa. And I don't need—or want—another man."

Ben shrugged. "Montoya's got a record."

Then her father had known about Cade all along. She decided to say nothing about Cade's visit that morning. Any further questions might arouse her father's suspicion. She would pry the information about Cade Montoya's prison record from her father at a more appropriate time. Studiously she stroked the errant curls from Davey's forehead, saying only, "That kind always does have a record."

Ben reached for his tobacco. "Somehow he doesn't seem like 'that kind,' Cassie. And something tells my old bones that this isn't going to be a peaceful summer."

Cassie slowed the pickup as she passed the old Cantu Grocery Store. The chipped-plaster green-stucco building had gone out of business years ago with the construction of a futuristic supermarket. But that hot afternoon a number of men and women, mostly the Mexican-Americans who inhabited the county, sauntered in and out. It was Saturday, and also the weekend of the Spring Chile Festival, which explained the mass of people walking the one main street.

And Cassie knew what explained the line of people streaming like ants through the derelict grocery store's rusted and warped screen door—Cade Montoya. Her father had reported that the man had set up headquarters there for his newly formed Hidalgo County Farm Workers Association. "Jonathan Reinhart ain't going to like it one bit," her father had finished ominously.

"You know how impossible it is to organize seasonal farm workers," Cassie had reminded him. "Others have tried to unionize the migrants before and failed."

"But they didn't have a Cade Montoya running the show," Ben had pointed out—as if that said everything about the man.

It should have said everything. She could dismiss him as one of the host of rabble rousers that periodically assailed Hidalgo County; this one just had a touch of charisma the others had lacked. A touch? When she was around him, it was like a blowtorch had been turned on.

Irritated with her train of thought, she pressed the pickup's gas pedal and sped on past Cantu's grocery toward the fairgrounds at the far end of Lordsburg. An arcade of booths had been erected among the old adobe buildings that ringed the grounds and served as refreshment centers. In these gaily decorated booths the craftsmen of Lordsburg set up their carvings and paintings, and the women displayed their baked goods and preserves. Quick-talking barkers enticed the young with games of chance, while the old-timers sought the shadows to drink their beer and exchange their yarns.

Here Cassie had brought Davey. Isolated by ranch life, Davey was enthralled with the festivities. Like one of the brightly colored helium-filled balloons, he practically floated from booth to booth. Mustard from a foot-long hot dog smeared his mouth, and cotton candy pinked his nose. As she and Davey threaded their way through the crowd, heads turned and people stared. The tow-haired son and mother, a rarity in that region of dark coloring, were startlingly beautiful—a cherub in ice-cream-dappled jeans and a Raphael-like madonna in a watercolor print sundress.

By the time the setting sun had spun its last web of light Davey's lids were drooping with exhaustion, and Cassie was ready to go home. Only the coronation of the Chile Queen and the dance that followed remained, and she was more than willing to pass them up. However, a note from her father on the pickup's windshield instructed her to stop by his office on her way home.

The Hidalgo County Sheriff's Department occupied one half of the small cinderblock jailhouse. From behind the counter the radio dispatcher, a short, bald Mexican national, greeted her with an enthusiastic, "Hi'ya, *señora!*"

"Hi, Hernandez. My father in?"

"You betcha."

With Davey in tow, she pushed through the counter's swinging door. The unmarked door to the sheriff's office stood open, revealing a bookcase filled with law enforcement manuals and a wall of file cabinets. She poked her head inside. "Am I on the wanted list, Sheriff?"

Ben looked up from the Offense/Incident report he was filling out. Behind him a display of framed certificates from various institutions testified to his expertise in the field of law enforcement. "Thought you might have escaped Lordsburg 'fore I caught you." He grinned.

Cassie settled into the hardbacked chair next to the old metal desk and pulled the sleepy Davey onto her lap. "That isn't likely, when my father's the sheriff. What did you need, Pa?"

He put the pen down and studied his daughter. She was breathtaking, with her mist gray eyes fringed with black and flaxen hair falling sleekly about her shoulders like a white Mexican mantilla. He said as much. "Too good-looking, Cassie, to be sitting home tonight. I'm finished here. I'll take Davey on home."

She rolled her eyes in mock hopelessness. "I

told you, I'm not interested in dancing or men."

"Humor an old man, eh, Cassie?" He rose from the desk and took Davey in his arms, cradling his grandson's head against his weathered cheek.

She made one last effort. "What if an emergency call comes in?"

"I'll take Davey with me. You know how he likes my siren and flashing lights. Now, go along with you, Cassie, gal. And bring back a husband!"

She wrinkled her nose at him and swept out of the office. She would stay a while, just for the crowning and one dance. Outside, she drew her white hand-crocheted shawl about her shoulders against the night's coolness. The fairgrounds were even more crowded now, and here and there she recognized people from her school days. It was the first time she had really been out for pleasure in the months since her return, and she greeted those who recognized her warmly. Initially they were hesitant about speaking to her, as if they stood in awe of her sophisticated beauty.

The once-pretty dark-eyed Anaberta, now plump and the mother of five, smiled shyly at first when Cassie paused to ask about her family, but then talked volubly. "My husband, the *cabron!*" she said, displaying in the phosphorescent light of the fairground's floodlights a gold-filled tooth. "He left me. Last time I heard he had a woman and was working the beet fields in Kansas. I take in other people's children now. Now I am like you, a *viuda*—a widow—no?"

There it was again—Widow Woman.

The coronation was held in the rodeo arena on a long platform wreathed with bright red *ristras* of chiles and illuminated by a red and green string of leftover Christmas lights. The girls vying to be the queen, most of them the high school's cheerleaders, posed for the last time in their formal gowns.

Cassie, watching the proceedings, stood alongside Marilyn Morton, a pixielike redhead who, after ten years, was still married to the co-captain of the football team. Her husband Curly now owned his father's drugstore, the only one in Lordsburg.

"Remember our senior year when I won Chile Queen?" Marilyn mused. "I was scared silly you would enter at the last minute and win—and Curly would end up your partner for the festival."

Cassie smiled. At seventeen she had thought her mouth too wide and her body too ungainly, though by her senior year she had lost most of her baby fat. But her figure then had been a far cry from the way she had appeared in a relatively recent lingerie ad that featured her in a black halter-neck teddy with a plunging back and high French-cut legs. Only a woman with long legs could have been accepted for that assignment.

"And I just wanted to leave Lordsburg," she told Marilyn. "Besides, Curly has had a yen for your red hair since we were all in the first grade."

History repeated itself as the mayor, in cowboy boots and string tie, announced a strawberry blonde as Lordsburg's Spring Chile Queen. At the burst of applause the young cheerleader gasped, gushed her thanks and cried. Immediately the mariachi band, resplendent in maroon and black charro suits trimmed with silver conchos and large black sombreros, launched into a round of "El Rancho Grande."

The festival was soon in full swing, with couples strolling toward the end of the grounds that had been roped off for dancing, and Cassie was ready to go home. However, Curly returned from the concession stands, precariously juggling three Styrofoam cups filled with more ice than lemonade. His curly brown hair had receded since their high school days, but he was still just as amusing. He told Cassie how the week before old lady Creighburg, the town's wealthy spinster, had upbraided him for the "girlie" magazines his drugstore stocked beneath the counter. "No doubt on Sunday the church congregation will stone Marilyn and me with chiles."

Cassie's soft laughter broke off at the sight of the man who strode purposefully toward her. Cade Montoya. She should never have come. She turned her back on him and rattled

off something about the festival to Marilyn.
But there was no escaping. Curly hailed the
man, saying, "How's the organizing going,
Montoya?"

Cade's eyes touched Cassie, and she felt a
slow heat stealing over her. "Better than I
expected. Usually the farm workers are apa-
thetic about organizing against injustices,
since they're transients. They figure that
before long they'll be hoeing another field
in another state, so whatever progress is
achieved won't help them."

Cassie tossed her empty cup in the nearby
trash barrel. "I guess I better start home."

"Not before I have a dance with you," Cade
said with a challenging grin. "It's only the
courteous thing to do for a stranger in
Lordsburg."

Cassie's glance appealed to Marilyn and
Curly for rescue. Too late she saw the matchmaker's gleam in Marilyn's eyes. Her friend
would be appalled if she knew the stranger
was an ex-convict.

"He's right, Cassie," Marilyn said. "It's the
least you can do." She gave Cassie a playful
push on the shoulder, and Cassie found
Cade's arm about her waist. He propelled her
toward the press of couples dancing slowly to
some romantic Mexican song played by a
haunting trumpet and the melodious strings
of a guitar and violin.

"I really don't dance," Cassie began.

"Then it's time you started." He pulled her

into the circle of his arms. She stiffened, trying to maintain some space between the two of them. "I wasn't convicted for rape," he teased, and pressed her against him.

She felt the solidity of his body. The muscles in his thighs that rubbed against her own and the muscles that bunched in his shoulders beneath her palm told her that he was accustomed to physical labor. His burnished skin could be an indication that he spent a lot of time in the sun. On a chain gang? "What were you convicted for?"

He looked down at her with a smile. "Ahhh, I have your interest now. Buy me a cup of coffee, and I'll tell you the story of my life."

"You don't have to tell me. I can pretty well guess. Sometimes you slip and let your education show when you speak. You graduated from college?"

"For sure."

"You were convicted of embezzlement. A bank teller—"

"Wrong."

"Why are you trying to organize the farm workers—the migrants and the Mexican-Americans?"

"Maybe because I was a migrant. Maybe because I'm half Mexican-American."

Then his heritage and not the sun accounted for his bronzed skin. She tried to judge his age, but his fierce features—the bladed nose and arrogant thrust of the jawline—made it difficult. He could have been anywhere from twenty-five to forty. Yet his self-assurance, his easy confidence that could come only from years of experience, led her to believe he was closer to the upper end of that scale.

His hand slipped lower about her waist to brace her hip against his. She tilted her head back and flashed him a withering glance. "Don't."

"You don't like dancing with a convict?"

"I don't like being pawed."

He threw back his head and laughed, deepening the faint lines at either side of his mouth. Irritated, her body went rigid. She tried to pull her hand from his, but he held it tightly. "There's a difference between being pawed and being held like a woman," he said more soberly, "and you should know it at your age."

She looked away from the eyes that probed her own. His words had thrust at a vulnerable part of her, momentarily weakening her, and she offered no resistance when his hand released hers and cupped the back of her head instead, pressing her face into the hollow of his neck.

"Nor was I convicted of manslaughter," he whispered against her ear. "So you have nothing to fear from me, Widow Woman."

"I'm not afraid," she mumbled against his neck.

"Then relax."

He was right, she thought with self-disgust. She was acting as spinsterish as Miss Creigh-

burg. Her free hand slipped up his chest to
join her other about his neck. She liked the
smell of his skin—a scent of shaving lotion
mixed with his man-odor. Imperceptibly her
awareness of this man blotted out all other
thoughts, sounds, sights. She was aware only
of him . . . the way his fingers tangled in her
heavy, straight hair . . . the way his other
hand clasped her hip, gently, yet with a firm
assurance that all but announced that it was
his right to hold her possessively.

She forgot for a moment that he was a
convict. Her body recalled passions that had
stirred within her during those first months
when Mario had courted her. She was totally
unconscious of the way her hips seemed to
seek contact with Cade's. She felt breathless
and lightheaded, as if she had just run the
Boston Marathon. Yet, illogically, she felt like
dancing all night.

She was jerked back to reality when he
halted and moved her slightly away from
him. She glanced up, and he nodded behind
her. She looked around to see Eric Reinhart.
Though Eric towered like some giant Viking,
Cade, in an indefinable way, seemed easily to
be the man's match.

In all other respects the two men were
totally unalike. Eric possessed a Nordic coloring that contrasted with Cade's Hispanic
darkness. The heir to Reinhart Farms wore
Western clothes that were expensive—modeling had taught her to recognize quality

clothing of whatever style. Cade's ensemble consisted of worn jeans and a cheap shirt of brown cambric. And Eric was very good-looking, whereas Cade—he was at once home-ly and handsome. If asked, she could not decide which.

"Dance, Cassie?" Eric asked.

Normally she would have turned him down with some polite excuse, as she always had in high school. But her response to Cade's overwhelming sensuality had surprised her, worried her. She nodded, accepting Eric's request.

Cade flicked her a glance of amusement, as if sensing her cowardice, and relinquished her to Eric. "You've changed," Eric said, taking her in his arms for the next dance. "Used to be a boy couldn't get near you."

His charge was true. She had seen too many high school couples who dated seriously and wound up at the altar with their first child on the way. Not for her. She had been deter-mined to escape what she had once thought of as stifling small-town life.

She didn't bother to reply to Eric's accusa-tion. She wanted only to finish the dance and go home. Unlike the other girls in Lordsburg, she had never had a crush on Eric—the hand-some, wealthy scion of the Reinhart dynasty. He had stirred no response in her. Even now, she danced impassively in his arms. For her Eric was like a seedless California grape, bred for appearance but lacking flavor.

Beyond him she glimpsed Cade. He was dancing with a sultry-looking young woman of undeniable beauty. Her flashing dark eyes laughed at something he said. Her brilliant white teeth were framed by crimson lips, just as her face was framed by gypsy-tossed raven hair.

"Who is she?" Cassie asked, nodding toward the petite but voluptuous-looking young woman, who wore a peasant blouse, tight jeans and stacked heels.

Eric followed the direction of her gaze. "Ramona Chavez. One of the migrant workers at Reinhart right now. And the man is—"

"I know. Cade Montoya."

His arm tightened about her waist. "Do you also know that he's a troublemaker? My foreman, Rico, tells me he's been in prison."

"I know that also."

"Then you know that dancing with him could ruin your reputation," Eric said harshly.

She glanced up at Eric. "I'm not the small-town girl you used to know. And I don't worry about what people in Lordsburg will say."

His mouth tightened. "You should."

"Why?"

"Because now that you're out of mourning, I mean for you to be my wife, Cassie. A Reinhart woman."

Her smile created dimples below her model's high-planed cheekbones. "And I mean to stay the Widow Woman."

Chapter 3

For what crime had Cade Montoya done time?

Cassie meant to ask her father when she returned to the ranch. The frame and native-rock house was ablaze with lights. She knew again that warm feeling of security that her childhood home held out to her—and to Davey. This was where the two of them belonged. She had made the right decision. She could see it in Davey's merry eyes and hear it in his laugh. Yes, she was content with her new life.

Nosing the pickup into the cluster of cottonwoods, she cut the motor and headed through the kitchen door, turning out the lights as she went. She passed Davey's room and peeked in. Her son's little bottom was tucked high in the air. She smiled and continued on to the living room. Her father was sprawled in the worn easy chair, his drooping mustache all but covering his mouth as he slept.

But when she gently shook his shoulder, he did not awaken.

Cassie's father had been sheriff of the county for almost thirty years, and he had known everyone. Almost the entire county seat turned out for his funeral.

Russian thistles, blown by the spring winds, tumbled across the hillock of parched earth that was being shoveled into the yawning hole. All eyes, however, were fastened on the deceased's daughter, who held her son's hand. Inappropriately, the people gathered in the barren cemetery were thinking not of the funeral, but of the stunning beauty of the bereaved daughter. Her finely-tailored black linen suit emphasized her svelte figure and the summer-white hair bound at her neck in a simple knot. Did she weep? None could tell, for the wide-brimmed hat dipped low, shadowing eyes as pale as morning mist.

The women sympathized, but their awe and envy of this exquisite young woman, who had returned from what was to them a fairy-tale world, created a gulf. And the men—they ached to comfort her.

One dared. But then, he was a Reinhart. And Reinharts dared anything in Hidalgo County.

"I'm sorry about your father," Eric said, touching her elbow to draw her attention from the workers who shoveled the earth. He placed his giant's body between her and the sand-pelting wind. "He was a good man. It will be hard to replace him as sheriff."

Cassie glanced up into the blue eyes that, even at that moment, seemed to indecently devour her. "It will be hard to replace him as a father," she said tonelessly and turned away. Davey, who understood little of what was going on, followed, his hand tightly clutching hers.

Then she saw him through the haze of swirling sand—Cade Montoya. He stood in the lee of a large, eroded headstone some distance from the other mourners. He was dressed in a dark blue windbreaker, and his shoulders were hunched against the sting of the sand, his hands jammed in his jeans. He saw her glance and nodded briefly, but made no move to approach her. Momentarily her curiosity was stirred to notice that Cade Montoya had come for the funeral when he was a stranger in town, but the press of people about her shut out her view, and ultimately her thoughts, of him.

Somehow she got through the rest of the day, talking politely to the stream of people who called at the ranch to offer their condolences. At last the remaining townsfolk left, the women taking with them their pans and baking dishes, empty now of cakes and roasts and pies. Cassie was left alone. Being alone didn't bother her. But the task that faced her—clearing out her father's clothes, going through his desk and accumulated papers—that was something she wanted to put off until another time. Yet it had to be done, and it would occupy her mind, keep her from grieving.

After she tucked Davey into bed she tackled her father's closet, heaping the overalls and boots and hopelessly dated shirts and ties into a pile that she would donate to the church. It was almost midnight when she got around to her father's desk. When she closed the desk drawers hours later sunlight was filtering through the calico curtains. Elbows braced on the scratched and stained desktop, she massaged her lids, then her temples, as she let the enormity of the debts she had discovered sink into her numbed mind.

Hay, vet calls, horseshoer, repairs, land taxes—a mound of bills that even the sale of horses would not cover. She would have to go back to work. But the modeling profession almost demanded that she be based in New York or Los Angeles, where the smog and pollution triggered Davey's asthma. What good would it be to keep the ranch if she and Davey couldn't live there? Always traveling, never at home to watch Davey grow, her private life exposed to the public eye—that was why she had quit.

There seemed to be no solution. She buried her head in the crook of her arm and wept for the first time—at her father's death, at the hopelessness of the situation—until weariness finally claimed her. Davey, poking her shoulder, woke her. His little toes peeked out from beneath his pajama legs. His buttercream curls were matted, and his eyes regarded her sleepily. He held out his hand to her. In it lay his grandfather's badge that she had found in the desk. "Are you the sheriff now, Mama?" he asked.

She ruffled his hair and smiled. "Of course not, Davey. Women can't be . . ."

Why not?

"Oh, Davey!" she cried, sweeping him up into her arms. "Out of the mouths of children! . . ."

"Why not?" she demanded of the four county commissioners. "Why can't you appoint me as sheriff in my father's place until the elections in November?"

Old man Haskell scratched his bald dome.

"Well, now, it ain't ever been done afore, Cassie. A woman sheriff just ain't protocol and such." She had known him all her life. As a child she had often perched on a stool in his Pullman car diner.

Purposefully she had worn a fashionably designed pair of khaki slacks and a severely cut tweed jacket to the county commissioners' meeting in order to play down the illusion of delicate femininity that she had sought to achieve in her modeling jobs. So much depended on their decision whether or not to appoint her as interim sheriff.

She stood alone in the courthouse room full of folding metal chairs that faced the long table where the county commissioners sat. She appealed to the other three commissioners now—the owner of the general store; a farmer; the town's one dentist.

"Where are you going to find anyone else as qualified as I am? How are you going to find a registered voter to fill in as sheriff when over half the county's population is made up of migrant workers and illegal aliens who come and go at will? Who else knows my father's duties as well as I do?"

Percy Duncan, the dentist, drew on his pipe. "This here job can be mighty dangerous. We'd feel responsible if something—"

"Dangerous?" Cassie almost hooted. "My father's last reported call was to find the Smiths' lost cow!"

"But what if you did have to use your gun?" asked the farmer, Hiram Blake.

"I'm not a marksman," she answered honestly, "but my father taught me to shoot well enough to hit beer bottles on a fence post."

She waited three agonizing days for the commissioners to reach their decision. Meanwhile she desultorily fed and groomed the horses, wrote thank-you notes for the wreaths and cards, cleaned the stalls, contacted creditors and snapped at Davey more often than she meant to.

The decision came, and it was positive—with a qualification: She was to attend the next minicourse in jail management, which would not be held at the Law Enforcement Academy in Santa Fe until sometime in July. But at least she could begin work immediately.

That night she took Davey out to celebrate. Other than Haskell's truck stop, Lordsburg had only a few restaurants that qualified for dining out. The most popular was the old adobe Hidalgo Hotel, at one time the only place to eat on the long stretch of road between El Paso, Texas and Tucson, Arizona. The Hidalgo required only casual dress, and she chose a simple shirtwaist of blue-striped oxford cloth that enhanced her figure.

"You can even have dessert," she told the excited boy as they took a booth near the back of the half-filled dining room. "After all, it was your idea that I become the town's sheriff."

Davey scrambled into the booth. "Can we light the candle, Mom?"

"As soon as the waitress takes our order." Her gaze swept the dining room for the waitress—and halted at the entrance. Cade Montoya stood there. His eyes locked with hers, and once again she felt the force of a white-hot current that seemed to sizzle between the two of them. She looked away, determined to ignore him and the feelings he generated in her.

"Have you decided on a name for our newest foal?" she asked her son, all the while very much aware of the man approaching their booth.

"X408," Davey answered.

"X408?" She grinned. "You've been watching those outer space movies on TV again."

Then Cade was standing before her. "Hello, Widow Woman."

She forced an even tone to her voice. "Please don't call me that."

"I had the feeling you liked being a widow."

Her fingers tightened about her water glass. He seemed to see past her cool facade too easily and to read her innermost thoughts. "That's not a very polite thing to say."

"Would you light our candle?" Davey asked. Cassie winced inwardly. No hope now that Cade would continue on his way to the bar.

"Sure, son." He withdrew a matchbook from his jeans and leaned across the table to remove the leaded globe. The flame lit the craggy contours of his face, casting his hazel eyes into darkness.

"Congratulations," he said after he capped the candle.

"For what?"

"You made the *Lordsburg Independent* this afternoon. The town's new sheriff, isn't it?"

"We're cele— we're celebra— we're having a party," Davey finished. "You want to have a party with us?"

"He probably has other dinner plans," Cassie interjected quickly.

Cade smiled, not bothering to hide his amusement at her discomfort. "I'd like that very much, son—unless your mother is worried about what people might say." He raised a brow, questioning her. "About my background?"

"Sticks and stones, Mr. Montoya. I don't worry about what people here say."

He slid into the booth next to Davey and faced her. "You know you'll be opening yourself to censorship when you pin on your father's badge?"

"Do you disapprove, Mr. Montoya?"

"Cade. Not at all, but the town's old biddies will. Are you prepared to handle all the talk?"

"Of course. Living in New York taught me to handle anything."

"Oh?" He withdrew a pack of cigarettes from his workshirt and tapped one out, offering her one. She shook her head. "What did you do in New York?"

She could have throttled herself. Rarely did she give away tidbits about her past so easily. "I went to school there, among other things."

He lit the cigarette, and she watched his hands. Strong, callused, capable. "Such as?"

"Getting married and having Davey," she said flatly. At that moment the waitress appeared. "Shall we order?" she asked, relieved at the interruption in a conversation that was getting too personal.

While they waited for the food Davey monopolized the conversation, and every time he opened his mouth she hoped that he wouldn't say any of the embarrassing things children quite often do. He did. "My mommy doesn't have a husband. Are you one?"

"No, I'm not," Cade said solemnly.

She wanted to slide beneath the table. Fortunately the waitress returned just then with the food. Cade ground out a half-smoked cigarette in the glass ashtray and asked, "Have you been a widow long?"

"Have you been a migrant worker long?" she countered.

His lips curved in a smile. Its beauty took her breath away. "Point taken."

Strange, he had made none of the predatory male's obvious passes to which big-city life had accustomed her—nor the more boldly flirtatious remarks that Eric would have made. Yet, perversely, she was highly aware of him as a man. It was as if the fine, almost-invisible hair on her body served as a receiver for some unseen signal that this man transmitted.

"Have you ever seen a baby horse?" Davey asked. "We just had one you could see. She's shiny black and all wet."

"I would like that, Davey." Cade's eyes flicked to Cassie. "You raise horses?"

"Quarter horses." She poked her fork at the salad the waitress had set before her. Horses were a safer subject than husbands. "It's only a small operation—fifteen mares and a stud. My father started the business to supplement his sheriff's income."

"And you intend to serve as county sheriff and operate a horse farm all on your own?"

She shrugged. "Why not? My father did it."

"Your father didn't have Davey to care for."

"I assure you, Mr. Montoya, that I'm quite capable. I had responsibilities both inside the house and out when other children were going to Friday night football games or Saturday afternoon movies."

Across from her Cade Montoya's eyes shadowed over. "For sure," he said softly; then, smiling, "Do you have chores to do around the house, Davey?"

Davey grinned, exhibiting a mouthful of baby teeth. "I take out the trash for Mama to burn."

Cade nodded soberly. "That's very big of you."

"Would you come see our baby horse?"

"Foal," Cassie corrected, hoping to take Cade's mind off the invitation.

Cade's smile dared Cassie. "I'll come by to see your foal one day soon, Davey."

The oil rig was silhouetted against the hot May sky like a giant denuded tree. Cassie turned the county's Ram Charger off onto the Lancet #3 service road and swung by the new drilling rig. It was part of her daily tour of duty—along with county roads, the copper-smelting plant in Playas, cattle ranches, farms, campgrounds. Even speeding tickets were part of her domain, though speeders were few in a region dominated by siestas and a slow pace.

Since she was the lone sheriff in the enormous county, her job demanded a six-day work week, with official hours from eight to five, but the county was sparsely populated and her tours of duty were made relatively easy.

She loved the vast untouched spaces of the country, where at night there were no distracting city lights to pale the brilliant shooting stars that arced across the sky. This was the land of Geronimo and Pancho Villa, of mining camps and Indian ruins and ghost towns. The winters were short and mild, the summer days hot; but the nights there on the high desert were cool and refreshing.

She slowed the four-wheel-drive vehicle and waved to the drilling foreman up on the rig's floor. The raw-boned young man doffed his hardhat and waved it, grinning. "Got time for a box lunch?" he yelled down.

"Not today," she called back and, waving, gunned the four-wheeler back down the dusty road.

She was surprised by how much she really enjoyed the job of sheriff. The duties allowed her the freedom of the outdoors and allowed her to wear the comfortable clothing she preferred. No uniform. Just the straw Stetson, jeans, boots and a casual Western shirt—all of which were almost a requirement, since she never knew when she would be called on to scramble down a bluff to rescue a stranded javelina hunter in the nearby mountains or untangle a calf from a barbed wire fence.

Then, too, she wore her father's .357 magnum strapped to her waist and anchored to her right thigh by a rawhide string. The shotgun that she used for close-range target shooting and the rifle for distances were kept in the rear of the vehicle. She doubted that she would ever have to use them, but she hoped that she could, should the need arise. The lariat for rescue work, the first-aid kit, the heavy handcuffs, leg-irons and belly chains—since childhood she had been more familiar with these accouterments of a sheriff's office than she had with her dolls.

How could a doll provide as much entertainment as the daily adventures she had experienced on her tours of duty with her father? As he had reminded her, she had more often than not run wild, barefooted and with wind-tangled hair bleached by the desert sun. Maybe that was why her parents had been so adamant about her music lessons, her one contact with a more civilized world.

The dispatcher on her two-way radio cut across the silence of the afternoon. *"Señora,"*

Hernandez drawled, "the Creighburg woman
—she reported a drunk. He's sleeping on her
front porch swing."

Cassie picked up the mobile unit's mike.
"I'll swing by," she told him.

Her father had hired the man, who was an
illegal alien, three months earlier, against
public opinion. "No one else to fill the bill,"
she had overheard him tell the newspaper's
editor. "And he speaks better English than
most of us."

"But, Duval, you know it's against the law
for a Mexican national to work without a
green card," the editor had pointed out.

"Nope. Not the state law. It's a federal
violation, and that's not my department."

And so Hernandez stayed on, doing an excellent job, Cassie thought. She only hoped
that she would be as compassionate a sheriff
as her father had been.

Within fifteen minutes she had cruised
down Lordsburg's main street and turned off
onto one of the few residential drives with
trees. Stout, double-chinned Miss Creighburg,
the matriarch of Lordsburg society, such as it
was, waited in front of her two-storied pristine
white-brick house. She tapped her gold-
knobbed cane impatiently against the
cracked cement sidewalk.

Cassie got out of the car. "Where is he, Miss
Creighburg?"

The old woman pointed the cane indignantly toward the porch. "There! What kind of

town has Lordsburg become when a woman has to worry about vagrants sleeping on her front porch?"

Cassie didn't answer, just cut across the well-watered grass to the porch. Behind her came the spinster, snapping, "If we had a man for a sheriff, we wouldn't have to worry about a vagrant wandering into town in the first place. Your father never would have allowed this."

Cassie gritted her teeth. She couldn't afford to antagonize the woman. "I assure you that he'll be taken care of, Miss Creighburg."

The old man, who snoozed on the swing with his mouth open, had a three-day growth of gray beard on his slack jaws, and his stained and dusty clothes reeked of mescal. Cassie tugged at the man's bony shoulders. "Come on along," she told him. "I've got a cooler place for you to sleep off your hangover."

"Huh . . . what?" he asked fuzzily.

He was a dead weight against her shoulder as she half pushed, half pulled him toward the steps and the four-wheeler. "And a free meal, too," she added. Behind her, old lady Creighburg slammed the front door.

Hernandez's rubicund face broke into a smile when she propelled the vagrant through the office door. "You want I should lock him up, *señora*?"

"I want badly that you should lock him up," she wheezed. The old man had to weigh a ton

and couldn't have had a bath in at least two
months.

Hernandez, who barely reached the drunk's
shoulder, prodded the old man across the
hallway that separated the sheriff's department from the cells that were used for up to
thirty days' detention only. Criminals accused
of felonies were sent on up to Las Lunas,
which was used as a reception area for the
Santa Fe Penitentiary.

Criminals.

The word made Cassie think of Cade Montoya again. He was not an ordinary man. Had
he ever been married or had children? She
doubted it. Something told her that he was a
wandering man. She recalled the country-
western song that advised, "Women who love
wandering men should never wear mascara."
She wasn't about to make that mistake.

That morning she had driven by the old
Cantu grocery. A great number of people continued to drift in and out, and a telephone
truck had been parked at the curb. On the
building itself now hung a large hand-painted
placard—Hidalgo County Farm Workers Association. He was serious about fighting the
growers for better labor rights. He was fighting a losing battle. No one ever won against
the growers. But Cade Montoya was no concern of hers.

Or so she told herself as she drove to Anaberta's house to pick up Davey. Since Anaberta's husband had deserted her, the woman

was delighted to have the income that came from having another child to care for during the day. And the arrangement worked out well for Cassie, since Davey had other children to play with for a change.

He scampered out of the immaculate one-bedroom house when Cassie drove up and threw his arms around her. "Mama!"

It was the best part of the day, holding her small son in her arms and showering kisses on his cherubic face. Things should have gotten better from there, but more problems faced her when she and Davey returned to the ranch. The pressurized water line that had replaced the old pump in the kitchen when she was a child had backed up. She had forgotten to thaw the hamburger meat for dinner. And she had yet to feed the stabled mare who was ready to foal.

Davey turned on the television, and Cassie's gaze picked up the dust that coated its top. Recalling that the windmill had lost a blade, that the dirty clothes were mounded beside the washer in the garage, and that the first-of-the-month bills were yet to be paid, she closed her eyes and sighed before heading for the stables. The horses came before dinner, dusting or washing.

When she reached the stalls Lady was already foaling. The mare lay on her side, panting. Her coat glistened with sweat, and she emitted an occasional whinny of misery. Cassie knelt beside her in the moldy hay and stroked her velvet-soft nose. "It'll be all right, Lady. I'll stay up tonight to help."

But Cassie knew that things were not going to be all right. She couldn't continue to hold down two full-time jobs and still be a proper mother. She was spreading herself too thin. She was always tired, and she yelled at Davey too often these days. Yet she knew she would never return to New York and modeling. That night, as she sat up with the mare, she made her decision.

The next afternoon, after she had answered the two complaints called in that day, completed her tour of the countryside and ordered the monthly laundry and food service any future jailed inmates would require, she took the step she had been dreading but knew was necessary. She drove to the new office of the Hidalgo County Farm Workers Association.

What if Cade Montoya wasn't there? What if he had left town?

The screen door squeaked when she entered. She halted just inside the door until her pupils focused. The first thing she noticed was the large red flag with the squared-off black thunderbird in the center that was tacked to the far wall. Below it, scripted in arabesque, were the initials HCFWA. The only furniture in the outer room was a badly scratched file cabinet and a cheap pine desk that looked as if it were pre–World War I vintage. Behind it worked the sultry beauty that Cassie had noticed at the dance, Ramona Chavez.

The girl glanced up, her pencil poised over the sheaf of papers before her. Her dark eyes narrowed. "Yes?" she asked with an accent that seemed to purr.

"Cade Montoya, please."

Ramona's gaze fixed on Cassie's badge before sliding down her jean-encased hips to halt on the pistol strapped to one thigh. The girl's lips curled mutinously. "The sheriff is calling?"

"Yes."

Ramona jerked her head over her shoulder, disturbing the ebony cloud of hair about her head. "Cade—Mr. Montoya—is in there."

Cassie's boots clicked across the bare concrete floor as she made her way to the office that was partitioned off by sheetrock that had yet to be taped and bedded. A monk's cell could not have been more stark. But then, Cade should be used to cells, she thought dryly. He sat with one leg hooked over the edge of a pine desk just as ramshackle as Ramona's. A telephone was cradled in the crook of his shoulder while he scrawled on a steno pad. As always, he was dressed in an old workshirt with frayed cuffs rolled to his elbows and time-softened jeans that hugged the lower half of his muscular torso.

What would it be like to have that muscular torso crushing . . .

She shook off the prurient thought. As though sensing her presence, he looked up and raised a questioning brow. "I'll come back another time," she said, relieved at the reprieve.

He put his hand over the telephone's mouthpiece. "No. I'm almost finished."

She remained standing in the doorway, waiting. He exchanged a few more words on the telephone and hung up. "Sit down," he said, indicating the vinyl chair in need of immediate reupholstering that stood beside the desk. "Or else I'll believe you *are* afraid of me."

"Hardly." She crossed to the chair. Not afraid. But wary. Wary of the effect this man had on her.

None of the handsome, sleek men she had posed with for advertisements and commercials had ever generated the response in her that he did—the way her skin surface seemed to take heat, the way her breath shortened as if her lungs had suddenly ceased to function.

None of those male models' effete good looks could compete with the power-stamped features of Cade's rugged face—the jutting slash of cheekbones, the nose that looked as if it had been broken in a fight, the winged nostrils that flared sensuously. His lips were singularly beautiful, with a reckless slant to them that was restrained by the faint grooves of patience that had been carved at either side. And, of course, there was the tantalizing pit in the center of his chin that almost dared her forefinger to touch it. With an effort, she restrained herself.

He leaned forward, his hand braced on one knee. "Why do you wear your hair tucked up under your hat like that?"

Involuntarily she pushed back the hat brim that dipped low over her eyes. Her lips curved in a self-mocking smile. "It's part of the illusion I seek to create. Citizens seem to feel that a man is better qualified to serve as a sheriff."

He nodded, but didn't take his eyes off her lips, which caused her to unwittingly moisten them with her tongue. "I see."

She wondered if he did see. If he understood the additional pressure that rode on her shoulders because she was a woman doing what was considered a man's job.

"Tell me, Mrs. Garolini, to what do I owe the honor of your visit?"

She almost jumped out of the chair. "How did you know my name?"

He shrugged. "The Chamber of Commerce might have mentioned it when I filled out the miles of red tape for HCFWA."

Of course, they would know it. She just wasn't used to being called by her married name. It was usually sheriff, *señora* or— behind her back—Widow Woman. "I—you mentioned once needing a part-time job—for room and board."

"Yes?"

He was making it difficult for her. She shifted uncomfortably in the chair. "I need help at the ranch," she grudgingly admitted. "Mornings, mostly."

He straightened and took a pack of cigarettes out of his shirt pocket. He lit one and softly tapped the matchbook against the desk top. The smoke he exhaled obscured his eyes, so she couldn't tell what he was thinking.

"Why don't you say something?" she demanded, resenting his silence.

"Things have changed since I . . . uh, applied . . . for the job."

"You don't need it anymore?" she asked, trying to keep the disappointment from her voice.

"I need it badly. With seven children, Armadeo doesn't need another mouth to feed. And this—" he negligently indicated the papers scattered across his desk—"doesn't pay a fiddler's dime."

"Then why can't—"

"Your situation has changed." He dropped the cigarette on the cement floor and ground it out with his shoe. "Your father is dead. You're alone in the house, except for Davey."

"And?"

"People will talk. Are you prepared for that?"

"I told you that Lordsburg gossip never bothered me before."

He leaned forward. "But your job may depend on your good name. It could be sullied— the Widow Woman living with the ex-convict." He smiled wickedly. "What a juicy scandal that would make."

She tore her gaze away from his unwavering scrutiny and fastened it on the state map pinned on the wall behind him, not really seeing the colored tacks dotting the areas owned by the large growers. She was on the horns of a dilemma, but she had no alternative. She would have to trust the citizens to judge her solely on her performance as sheriff.

Unflinchingly her gaze met Cade's steady one. "How soon can you move in?" she asked.

Chapter 4

"IT'S ABOUT YOUR NEW HIRED HAND."
Marilyn's voice carried over the telephone in
an urgent and low tone, as if she thought
Cade Montoya could overhear her. "Is he
there now?"

"He's outside." With the receiver braced in
the hollow of her shoulder, Cassie stood before the kitchen sink, scooping the soft-boiled
eggs from their shells. She wished Marilyn
would hurry, or she would be late with
Davey's breakfast. "What about him?"

"Cassie—he's an ex-convict! Percy Duncan
himself told me yesterday when I went to
have a tooth capped."

"I already know that, Marilyn."

She glanced out the kitchen window, her
eyes seeking Cade's brawny figure. In the

week since he had moved in, he had proved
what a hard, capable worker he was. By six-
thirty, after a quick cup of coffee, he could
usually be found working around the barn.
And he seemed to have a feel for horses, as
though he might have worked around them
before.

Her eyes found him now, hunkered down by
the nearest section of barbed wire fence. He
was cleaning out the tumbleweed that had
tangled in the wire. Pee Wee sat at his side,
his tail swishing. Her gaze feasted on the play
of the muscles in Cade's forearms. The fluidi-
ty of his movements was almost phenomenal.
She was reminded of those restless, intensely
muscular figures sculpted by Michelangelo, or
one of Rodin's works like *The Kiss*. . . .

"Did you hear me, Cassie?"

"What?"

"I asked what he had done time for."

"I have no idea."

"You mean you didn't check?"

"No." She could have used the computer
bank, but now . . . now that he was living in
the same house with her . . . it was like snooping. Her sense of integrity prevented her from
doing something like that. Somehow, she
trusted him. Or perhaps, a small voice said,
she didn't want to know because she might be
forced to discharge him. A worker of his capa-
bilities was exactly what she needed around
the ranch. But the small voice asked if that
was the only reason. Why had she checked in

the mirror only that morning to make certain her jeans didn't cup her derriere too tightly and lamented the fact for the first time in years that her mouth was far too wide? She had long ago ceased to be concerned about her looks, except from a professional point of view.

"He could have done something horrible, Cassie. It's not safe to be there alone with a man like that, you know."

Cassie added a pat of butter to the eggs, saying, "I'm sure I can take care of myself."

"But people are going to talk. A man like that living in the same house with you is going to delight gossips like old man Haskell and Miss Creighburg."

Cassie sighed. A man like that—that was the problem. "Marilyn, if Cade Montoya were a hunchback, nobody would care that we're living in the same house together."

"Well, I'll set the old gossips straight if anything is said within my hearing. But, Cassie, do be careful."

Cassie said goodbye and hung up. But when she went to call Davey for breakfast, Cade stood just inside the kitchen doorway. "Oh! I didn't hear you come in," she sputtered. How much had he overheard?

The lines at either side of his mouth twitched, but all he said was, "It looks like some stretches of the fence haven't been replaced since the great range wars, the barbed wire's so rusted. You want me to pick up a spool today when I go into town?"

Nervously she reached for the terry dish towel on the refrigerator handle and wiped her hands. "Tell Alice to charge the spool to the ranch account." Would she ever catch up on all the bills?

He walked toward her, and she stiffened, her eyes guarded. When he took the dish towel from her hands, she gasped, "If you—"

He rubbed the towel just under her cheekbone. "You've got egg yolk smeared on your face."

It was said in such an offhand manner that she was certain he hadn't known of her preliminary panic—until he smiled. His strong teeth were a brilliant white against his bronzed skin, and slightly uneven, which somehow contributed to the rakish charm of his smile. Still, she was furious with him. He had found her momentary fear amusing.

She snatched the dish towel from him. "I've got to wake Davey."

That night at the dinner table he made an oblique reference to the morning's episode, saying, "You should keep the house locked, Cass—even when you're here. You never know when someone might walk in."

Her knife and fork butchered the chicken-fried steak. One week, and already the tension of living in the same house was beginning to tell on her. "You sound just like a tyrannical husband," she snapped without looking up.

It was the wrong thing to say. "Are you going to be our new husband?" Davey piped up.

"No, he is not!" she blurted. She caught the flicker of amusement in Cade's eyes before he ducked his head and vigorously attacked his steak. She could have sworn he had to clear his throat of laughter before he next spoke. "With the work here taking up my mornings, I'll be working late in the evenings at the headquarters. So it'd be best not to fix a plate for me at dinner time."

"Aww, gee," Davey said, pouting his rounded little mouth in disappointment.

Cassie tried not to show her relief. "You really mean to push for a strike this summer, Cade?"

She purposely spoke with the condescending formality of employer to employee, and Cade chose to mock her by responding in colloquial speech. "For sure. Reckon that's the only way to beat these Reinharts."

She stifled her irritation. "Just how does one go about setting up a strike?"

As though he sensed that her question was genuine, he replied candidly, "For the strike to succeed in its purpose, the tactical questions that have to be settled are more difficult than most people really realize. We have to station pickets around the fields being

worked. It's their job to persuade at least one
worker—all we need is one—to walk off the
job and give his name to the U. S. Department
of Labor agents assigned to the area. Then a
labor dispute would be certified and a strike
declared. You see, an official dispute gives a
union a legal basis for prosecution, since to
use a green card laborer to break a strike that
has been certified—as Reinhart has always
done before—is against the law."

"You won't find anyone with the courage to
defy Jonathan Reinhart. Jobs are too scarce
here."

He shrugged. "Quite often it's the last person you would expect who suddenly says, 'I've
had enough,' and walks off the field."

Caravans of ancient cars had begun appear-
ing daily on the county roads, and she knew
that the spring chile planting would begin
next week. The gasoline gypsies would be
applying for the various positions—mostly
hoers, but also tractor drivers and fertilizer
sprayers and, later in the season, irrigators,
pickers and box checkers. The town would be
an anthill of activity—and, with Cade Montoya in town, a hotbed of trouble, just as her
father had predicted.

What had she gotten herself into?

Cassie looked up from the supplemental
report she was filling out on Lost/Stolen Live-
stock. Hernandez's usually bird-bright eyes

were flat as he stood in the doorway, shifting from one foot to the other, waiting for her to acknowledge him.

"Yes?" she asked.

"Señor Eric—he is here, waiting to see—"

Eric Reinhart towered behind Hernandez. "Cassie, what's this I hear about Montoya staying out at your place?" the blond giant demanded.

She regarded him coolly. "He works for me."

Eric ignored Hernandez's disapproving glare and strode into the room, bracing his palms flat on her desk. "Montoya's a professional agitator."

Her lips flattened. "Do you want to file a complaint? If so, Hernandez will give you the necessary forms."

"I want you," he said tersely. "I want to take those damn pins from your hair and watch it tumble about your shoulders. For God's sake, Cassie, I want to marry you! I want you to be Mrs. Eric Reinhart."

For the first time she smiled. This she could handle. "Sorry, Eric, but I don't intend to remarry."

He sighed and straightened. "I don't give up easily, Cassie."

"I know. The smaller farmers you and your father have bought out testify to that."

Eric's eyes, blue as Scandinavian fjords, scowled. "That's exactly my point. The smaller farmers wouldn't be forced into selling if it weren't for the periodic strikes staged by troublemakers like this Montoya. Reinhart Farms and the other large growers can afford to weather the financial havoc caused by agitators like him."

"Then why all the concern?"

"He's gone a step further." Eric waved his hand in the direction of the street. "He's set up a headquarters. Organized my former workers—my very own workers! Hell, Cassie, he's even set up infiltrators who know when the crews'll be working the roadside fields. He and his subversive monkeys are out there right now with bullhorns exhorting my workers to leave the fields and strike."

She tapped her pencil impatiently. "It's perfectly legal, Eric."

"Until he sets foot on my property, it is. And I want you out there to arrest him when he does."

"I've got more important things to do than sit out at Reinhart Farms, waiting to see if Cade Montoya commits a misdemeanor."

This time Eric planted his knuckles on her desk, leaning over it. "My father wants him arrested, Cassie," he said softly and stalked from the room.

A moment later Hernandez materialized in the doorway, reminding her of some magical gnome. "You wanna *aspirina, señora*?"

She smiled grimly. "How about forty?" She rose and reached for the straw hat on the treestand. "I'm on my way out to Reinhart

Farms. If anything should come up here, you can reach me on the mobile unit."

Hernandez's rubicund face closed over. "That old man Reinhart no good, *señora*. He work the farms with Mexican labor because us *mojados* are here illegally, and he knows we are defenseless. We are afraid to fight for better conditions, or we lose our jobs—the money we need bad—to others."

"I know that, Hernandez."

It was an old argument, one that she had heard often before. The wetbacks who illegally crossed the border needed the work badly and would work for any pay, would do demeaning work that other workers would turn down, preferring instead to wait in line for unemployment checks.

Hernandez, fortunately, was slightly better educated than his *compadres*. Incredible as it sounded in the modern age of awareness and social reforms, Hernandez, she had learned, was saving to buy his girlfriend from a Juarez brothel, to which she had been sold to pay her parents' debts. Though he was technically breaking a federal law by working in the United States, she also knew that she would find it very difficult to replace a person of his diligence and loyalty.

And, as much as she disliked the Reinhart family's domination of Hidalgo County, she recognized the fact that she had an obligation to at least drive by and check out Eric's complaint. Yet as she drove out through the ironwood- and mesquite-studded Pyramid Valley, she knew that she would rather face Eric Reinhart's bluster any day than Cade Montoya's quiet determination that was becoming more and more evident in the greater flow of people in and out of his busy headquarters. Despite his casual, easy-going life-style, she dimly perceived in Cade a relentlessness and ruthlessness when it came to something he wanted badly enough.

As she neared the denser area of farms, her surroundings took on a surrealistic aspect. Dust rimmed the horizon, blotting out Granite Peak. Water from the artesian wells seeped across the desert floor in endless concrete trenches. It was a man-made landscape—a soft sea of dusty foliage coated with organophosphates and chlorinated hydrocarbons.

A chain of crippled cars presaged the site that was being picketed. As she drove nearer she could hear mariachi music, scratchily played, as if recorded, and people singing, presumably a union song. A picketer waving a banner with the red-lettered word *"Huelga"*— strike—stepped out from between two of the parked cars to walk to the highway's far shoulder—no-man's-land. Maybe a score of people, mostly Mexican-Americans and all wearing the red strike handkerchiefs about their necks, lined the shoulder, waving and shouting, urging the workers to leave the fields and strike.

Most of the workers continued with their jobs, stooping every few feet to plant the chile seeds along the rows that snaked through the fields. But a few looked up, listened—as if the longing to go over had stirred in them—and then, weakened by the desperate need of a job, turned back to their labor. Here and there children straightened on their spindly shanks to listen to the diverting music before their parents' hissed commands sent them back to work.

One woman, who was possibly Cassie's age, with a baby carried in a sling on her back, actually took several steps toward the line of strikers at the side of the road until Rico, the corpulent Reinhart foreman, snapped something that Cassie was unable to hear. The woman's head drooped, and she retraced her steps to the nearest gondola of chile seeds.

The planting of the chile seeds was back-breaking labor that, unlike the harvesting, could have been automated—but that would have cost far more than what Reinhart paid for manual labor.

Cassie closed the Charger's door and crossed to the line of picketers. Some wore chest boards with the same red lettered *Huelga*. A scrawny woman in *huaraches*, with soles made from rubber tires, shouted through the bullhorn. *"Vengase, señores,"* she bawled, *"para su respeto y dignidad. Leave the fields. Hold your heads high. Don't be afraid of the *patron*. Vengase!"*

Along the picket line Cassie spotted the wiry frame of Armadeo, Cade's captain. She was aware of the distrustful eyes turned on her as she made her way to him. A badge too often elicited that baleful response. Armadeo, who wore a union button, looked up at her approach and nodded at his pickets to continue.

"Hello, Armadeo," she said cordially. She had always liked this man with the mild, boyish appearance and quiet dignity. "Where's Cade?"

He pocketed the note pad he held. "Hello, Sheriff. Last time I saw Cade he was on the phone with some community service in Santa Fe—or maybe it was the Department of Health. He may be out at the migrant camp delivering medicine by now."

"Medicine?" she asked, incredulous.

Armadeo shrugged. "Sure. Sometimes different health care services provide medicine for the indigent."

She nodded toward the workers. "You know, don't you, Armadeo, that it's against New Mexico law for the picketers to be closer than fifty feet apart? Technically, I would have to make a few arrests here."

He pointed to a farm truck some two hundred yards down a dusty, private side road. The truck looked as if it had been in a demolition derby. "Then you better start by arresting Rico, Sheriff. He arranges for the transportation of the migrant workers from the camp to the fields in that unlicensed heap."

She repressed a conspiratorial smile. Armadeo might not have finished school, but he possessed common sense along with an innate shrewdness and resourcefulness that were enviable. She could understand why Cade had chosen him for his captain. "I'll check into it. And, Armadeo—thanks."

He gave her a big, honest smile. "Much obliged, Sheriff."

She walked across a portion of dry, heat-shriveled soil toward Rico. A sign warned: NO TRESPASSERS. SURVIVORS WILL BE PROSECUTED.

The foreman, whose skin had a greasy sheen to it, lounged against the tailgate of a white pickup stenciled with the insignia of Reinhart Farms, a green silhouette of a lone, lush tree. The man was as fat and sedentary as the status quo that he was hired to represent.

"Want a drink, Sheriff?" he asked with a servility that bordered on insolence, then nodded at the fifty-gallon water can in the truck's bed.

She eyed the tin cup chained to the water can. No wonder hepatitis spread so easily. Everyone drank from the same cup. "Why don't you have paper cups for the workers?"

His shaggy brows rose innocently. "It is against the law?"

"No. But driving that farm truck without a license is. Get one, Rico, or I'll cite you."

His lids drooped; his thick lips curled in what was almost a leer. "I will see that it is done," he said in a sibilant voice that affected her like a fingernail scratching along a blackboard. "You will, of course, cite the workers for their offense—public use of bullhorns. Perhaps obstructing traffic, also?"

"I will warn them, as I warned you," she snapped and turned away. She would have to talk with Cade, an encounter she did not exactly look forward to.

The bathroom door swung open, and Cassie whirled. Cade stood there, brown and barbaric. His jeans were only partially zipped. She froze, her eyes fastening on the purple slash that made a ridge across his bare chest just below one nipple. Involuntarily intrigued, she let her gaze sweep over the bronzed flesh, roughened by an inverted triangle of thick, crisp hair that tangled its way downward from the button-hard nipples past the navel . . . before she remembered that she was even less covered than he. Rosy beige bikini panties and a matching lace-edged bra were all that shielded her from his heavy-lidded gaze.

She grabbed her towel from the tiled counter and clutched it before her. The score or so of nights that had passed with Cade sleeping in her father's room hadn't yet accustomed her to his presence, especially not at five-thirty in the morning. "Good morning," she said in a carefully controlled voice.

Beneath the sleep-tousled hair his yellow-ish hazel gaze glided over her, revealing nothing of his thoughts while seeming to take in everything about her—from her peach polished toenails to the smear of toothpaste on her lower lip. He smiled slowly, that charismatic smile that she had seen him give at the farm workers' rally. "For sure."

Then he closed the door, and she slumped weakly against the sink, her fingers gripping the counter's edge for support. Her gaze encountered the reflection, seemingly a stranger's, in the mirror. A wave of heat crimsoned the woman's cheeks, and her eyes glistened like those of someone dazed. Yet it wasn't actual fear that had triggered such a reaction, but wariness.

After years of modeling she was unsusceptible to the good looks of the smooth, sleek men who had posed with her. But Cade exuded an animal magnetism that hit her on a visceral level. She had fled New York in search of a settled life for her and Davey. Had she made a mistake in allowing Cade Montoya to come into that life?

Quickly she twisted her hair into a loose knot atop her head and donned her khaki slacks and kelly green, military-tailored blouse before hurrying to the kitchen. She was beating the eggs when Cade entered some minutes later. She detected the tangy scent of shaving lotion and glanced up. His thick, unruly hair had been smoothed back from his temples in an attempted part, but already curls were creeping forward to cluster about his jutting cheekbones.

"Coffee's ready," she said in what she hoped was a matter-of-fact voice as she turned away from him.

Behind her she heard his catlike tread across the linoleum floor. Unable to contain her fascination with this extraordinary man, she glanced covertly in his direction. He was leaning against the kitchen counter, barefoot, and with his legs crossed at the ankles, watching her as he sipped his steaming coffee. Above the rim of the coffee cup his winged nostrils flared sensuously. An amused smile curved his lips, the only soft feature in that irregular, rough-hewn countenance.

Hastily she returned her attention to the eggs, acutely aware that the beat of her pulse was keeping tempo with the rapid whirr of the wire wisk. She should talk to him about the strike he was agitating, but she didn't feel prepared to wage a verbal war yet—and with Cade's unrelenting attitude about the strike, she doubted it would be a pleasant conversation.

She began to rattle off words inanely. "We're getting low on feed. I'll pick up a bag when I'm in town. She Devil's been running the fence. You better check her. I figure she'll show to the stud soon."

"Yes'm."

She heard the amusement in his reply and blushed profusely. Realizing the delicacy of the subject she had launched on, she studiously scrambled the eggs in the cast-iron skillet as she selected another subject. "If you have time before you leave, could—"

"Cass."

The word, quietly but firmly spoken, halted her babble. The spatula she held ceased its agitated revolutions. He set the coffee cup down on the counter and crossed to her with that graceful roll inherent to the animal kingdom.

After taking the motionless spatula from her, he laid it aside and took her two slender hands into his larger one. "Cass, if I'm going to live here, to work here, you can't continue to fear me. The arrangement won't work."

"I'm not—"

He laid a callused but gentle finger on her lips, silencing her denial. "I did time—seven months about four years ago—when I was arrested in a nuclear waste protest march. Aside from a couple of self-protective scuffles inside Huntsville Penitentiary, I've never harmed anyone. And I won't harm you."

The memory of the purple scar that crossed his chest told her that he had minimized those "scuffles," yet instinct told her that he would not harm her. Still, she was affected by his nearness, by—absurdly—the gentleness in his touch. She recalled that he had accorded Pee Wee that same gentleness. Her eyes trained on his corded neck where the pulse beat faintly, she said, "I believe you. It's just that I'm unused to . . . another man in the house. Of course, Pa and Davey were—are—different."

"And your husband?"

She tugged her hands from his clasp and turned back to the briskly cooking eggs. Her throat was thick with the effort required for her to talk in a normal voice. "I—we were married for almost nine years. He was ill . . . dying . . . the greater part of that time."

"I'm sorry," Cade said.

She had thought she would never want another man in her life, but as she watched Cade head out to the barn . . .

Chapter 5

CASSIE KNEW THAT CADE WOULD COME IN much later, after she and Davey were already in bed. On the previous nights she had seen the spray of the kitchen light on the hall wall, listened to the refrigerator being opened and closed, and a while later heard the soft click of her father's bedroom door. She knew now that within the bedroom Cade not only read late into the night but also wrote—apparently voluminously, if the wadded lined yellow sheets in the plastic wastebasket were any indication. To whom did he write? Or were the sheets merely copious notations he made for the farm workers' organization?

Though she had intended to speak to him about the strike for two days now, she had cravenly temporized. She preferred to keep him at a distance. He was such an articulate man, and she knew that remaining impartial about the ever-widening rift between the growers and the farm workers would be difficult. Even their employer/employee relationship was difficult to maintain, perhaps because she sensed that he didn't recognize such a distinction, though he treated her with overt politeness.

And it was that politeness that inexplicably irritated her.

As she wrapped the remaining pieces of fried chicken in cellophane and tucked them away in the refrigerator, she puzzled over the kind of man she had hired. An activist, certainly. An idealist? Not to the point of ineffectiveness. A *man*, above all. An aura of basic, primeval masculinity emanated from him. And that was what made her so uneasy. Although Ramona Chavez was apparently quite comfortable in the man's presence. Were the two together now?

"Mama," Davey said, looking up from the coloring book he had spread on the kitchen table, "Pablocito has two fathers. Why don't I have any?"

Carefully she concealed her surprise. Pouring out the stale coffee, she asked in a noncommittal voice, "Would you like one, Davey?"

The boy bent his sun-kissed curls over the

coloring book and applied a magenta crayon to the page. "I don't know. No, I guess not. Maybe we can get a duck instead."

Her lips puckered in a smile that refused to be repressed. "A duck would be nice. But I think we would need a pond."

Davey's head never lifted from the page he was coloring. "Oh, I bet Cade would fix something for a duck. Why don't you talk to him 'bout it, Mama?"

"We'll see, Davey."

"Robles has started a fracas at The Road to Ruin." Hernandez's voice crackled over the two-way.

Cassie sighed and pressed the mike button. "I'm on my way, Hernandez."

The Road to Ruin, a *cantina*, backed up to a railroad spur in the seedier part of town, where the growers' warehouses, offices and packing sheds were located. As she approached the dung-colored building, she could hear a man's angry shouting above the music of the jukebox. Within the darkened *cantina* a neon beer sign flashed on and off, illuminating Robles's bearlike figure balanced precariously on one end of the old mahogany bar.

"Do you think the Anglo will help you?" he demanded of the men at the tables, some of whom were too drunk to focus on Robles, much less follow his speech. Robles waved the bottle in his hand. "Or this farm workers thing—will it help the poor Mexican-

American? No! It is only *La Raza* that will help us fight the growers."

Cassie made her way through the maze of tables toward the counter. Here and there a few heads snapped up at the sight of a woman entering the establishment. "Widow Woman . . . *La Viuda,*" could be heard among the murmurs. She had to smile that her marital status still made more of an impression than her professional status as county sheriff.

Robles, unaware of her presence, wove his way like some tightrope walker down the narrow expanse of the counter shouting, *"Viva La Raza!"*

The *cantina's* owner, a little man with a large mandarin mustache, hurried over to Cassie. "Please get him out," he begged her. "Before he starts a fight and destroys everything."

She walked to the end of the counter, where Robles teetered, still yelling drunkenly. The smell of rotgut mescal fumes overwhelmed her. Perhaps she should have been afraid, but her father had often maintained that even the meanest man, a man such as Robles, could be calmed with gentle words. Maybe that was why her father had never had to resort to his gun. She tried the same tactic now.

"Robles," she called up to him.

He blinked, jutting his head to peer at her more closely. "Widow Woman," he said thickly.

"Come on down, Robles. I want you to tell me about *La Raza*."

With exaggerated movements he dropped to a squatting position and scowled at her. "*La Raza*—it is not for white women . . . Widow Woman."

He laughed suddenly, contemptuously. But she said in a cajoling voice, "Then tell me why not."

He slid off the bar's edge and started to reach for another bottle of beer on the counter behind him. "'Cause it's for the—"

She reached the bottle first and handed it to him. "Because why?" she asked, gently tugging at his elbow as she steered his unsteady steps toward the front door.

He worked at the bottle's stopper, unaware of what she was about. "'Cause it's for us Mexican-Americans. *La Raza*—The Race—Brown Power, that's what it is."

The rest was easy—propelling him into the car, driving him to the courthouse while he raved on between swigs of beer. In an almost lachrymose tone he alternately talked of being fired from working the Reinhart Farms and raged that he would get even. But by the time she reached the county jail's parking lot, he was fast asleep. She filled out the arraignment papers and tucked him into a comfortable cell to sleep off his drunken discontent.

"I'm going over to the farm workers association," she told Hernandez. It was as good a time as any to talk with Cade about the association. Their off-hours never seemed to coincide. At least this way their discussion could take place in a business office rather than the isolated intimacy of her home.

Ramona seemed about as glad to see her as Robles had been. She tossed her gypsy-fluffed hair over her shoulder and said, "Cade is talking on the telephone."

"I'll wait," Cassie said, knowing that she was dashing the young woman's hopes that she would leave.

Another line rang, and Ramona turned to answer it. A row of metal chairs now backed up to one wall, and several workers, mostly men, sat there, twisting their hats in their hands while they waited. The office, small and cluttered, was busy, as the old grocery store had never been.

Before Cassie could take a seat Cade appeared in the doorway of his office. For a change he was dressed in slacks, but wore a pin-striped shirt that had seen better times. Even on such a busy day he seemed unhurried; he was altogether where he was. "Ramona, would you get me the number of the New Mexico migrant agency, and—" He broke off at the sight of Cassie.

He strode toward her. His presence seemed to obliterate everything else in the room. His lips danced in a warm, humorous smile. "Did I forget one of my chores?"

The effect that smile had on her was devastating. No wonder men and women alike were willing to follow his lead. "I would like to talk with you," she said.

His gaze settled on her lips, as if he would find there a clue to the woman she was. "Sheriff to citizen, or employer to employee?"

"The former."

Noting the seriousness in her tone, he said, "Ramona, cancel the call and get Armadeo to finish the interviews." And to Cassie, "I have to drive out to the migrant camp to deliver a voucher. Can we talk on the way?"

"We can take my car."

The four-wheeler was more like a tank than a car, but Cade seemed to diminish its spaciousness with a purely masculine force that disconcerted her. He laid his arm across the back of the seat, watching her as she pulled the vehicle out into the stream of traffic.

"Despite the way you hide your hair under that hat, Cass, you're a damned beautiful woman."

The way he said it—it was more a simple statement of fact than a compliment. Did he save flowery words for other women? For Ramona? "People too often think a beautiful woman incapable of thinking or acting intelligently," she replied with a thin smile, "so I desexualize myself."

He laughed in amusement. "Apparently you haven't looked in the mirror lately. Those jeans reveal more feminine assets than they hide."

His fingers tucked a stray tendril up beneath her hat band, and she shivered, not unpleasantly, at his touch. It was difficult to believe that that same hand had probably wielded a knife at another human—if the scar on his chest was any indication—and yet could touch her so gently.

"I arrested Robles today," she said quickly, trying to escape the direction her thoughts seemed to be taking lately. "He was campaigning for *La Raza* in a disorderly fashion—drunk."

"I hate to hear that," he said, though his tone indicated just the opposite.

She glanced at him. "Why? Being half-Mexican, I would think you would support that organization as well."

"*La Raza*, Black Panthers, Ku Klux Klan . . . any organization that promotes one segment of the human race rather than its totality goes along with Hitler's concept. It's dangerous. And Robles's misdirected anger could endanger the Hidalgo County Farm Workers Association."

"How?"

"I'm committed to nonviolence, Cass. Robles's kind know only violence. There are better ways to get the concessions we want from the growers."

"Such as?"

"Sloppy picking and packing. Slowdowns. Marking the boxes wrong—which fouls up the record keeping. Boycotts. The grape pickers in California gained their contracts more through boycotts than strikes."

"That's what I have to talk to you about. The pickets have committed some offenses for which Reinhart could demand their arrest."

"Sounds like you're siding with us."

She flicked him an annoyed glance. "I'm not siding with either faction. Only warning both sides. I won't have trouble here in Hidalgo."

"It's already here, Cass."

She refused to debate the issue and drove silently to the migrant camp that Reinhart had provided on a section of land that had been overworked. The people of Lordsburg called the camp a shantytown. As if the area had been polluted by nuclear fallout, no vegetation—no grass or trees—grew there. The triple rows of houses were little more than tarpaper shacks. Cade halted before a house with a junked car in a dirt-smooth yard. She remained in the car and watched him stride to the door to deliver the check he had secured from the New Mexico Department of Health. The recipient was a new member of the HCFWA, who had been injured on the job.

Cade talked briefly with the tired-looking wife, who had two young children clinging to her skirts. When he returned to the car Cassie said, "You haven't always picked crops, have you?"

He flicked her a glance and settled back in the seat. "What makes you think that?"

She wheeled the car out of the barren camp and back onto the highway. "The muscles in your arms and back—stooped labor doesn't develop such a powerful physique."

"I've always been a migrant," he answered evasively. "My family followed the usual flow of migrant workers. Texas, New Mexico, Colorado, California."

"But somewhere along the line you received a college education," she charged as she turned the car back onto Main Street.

He shrugged, the tendons and ligaments rippling across his back beneath the worn cotton material. "I went to college in the winter and worked the lumber camps on Smith River just south of the Oregon line during the summer."

That explained his superb build, she thought.

When he spoke next his deep voice held an uncustomary tense quality. "College was tough, because my education up to that point had been scanty. Always moving. A new school every few months. Sometimes picking instead of attending classes." He stopped abruptly, as if he had said more than he wanted to.

"If you weren't happy as a child of migrant workers, why do you continue?"

"Moving from one place to another is in my blood now, Cass. I could never settle down."

She considered that statement later after she let him off at the HCFWA office. Too often she found herself thinking of him. She would do well to remind herself that he did have migrant blood in him. Soon, when he had accomplished what he had set out to do in Lordsburg, he would be on the road again to some other migrant community.

She could only hope that Davey wouldn't grow too attached to Cade. As it was, Cade had already snared Pee Wee's undivided loyalty. No longer did the dog accompany her when she jogged in the mornings, which was getting to be less and less often as her sheriff's job demanded more and more of her time.

Yes, becoming involved with Cade, a man possessed with the wanderlust, could only spell disaster for her and Davey. So why then did she think of him so often? Why, at night, did she listen in the darkness of her bedroom for him to enter the house?

Grand Lady was ready to foal. "She's restless and pawing a hole in her bedding," Cassie told Cade as she handed him his morning cup of coffee. She was learning to prepare it as he liked it—black and as thick as molasses. And the more warmed-over the better.

The sun had not yet risen, and the dawn's quiet filled the white and yellow kitchen. For Cassie it was the most pleasant part of the day. Even more so now, with this strange man who had come into her life to share these peaceful, almost intimate moments.

Cade, his hard jaw shadowed by the morning's stubby beard, took the cup and shoved back the dark riotous hair that tumbled over his sleepy-lidded eyes. No doubt he had been up until the early hours of the morning, as usual. But doing what? When she cleaned his room she found no evidence of any books he could be reading. And her principles were too high to allow her to pry into her father's desk that Cade now used or the chest of drawers.

He gulped the steaming brew, and for the first time that morning his crooked grin appeared. "I think I'm going to make it, Cass."

That grin had the power to melt her bones. "Could you keep a check on Grand Lady this morning?"

"No problem. I was going to groom the horses today and clean the stalls anyway. I'll fill her stall with a fresh layer of wheat and rye straw."

He talked easily with her as she prepared Davey's breakfast, the kind of talk a husband and wife would share. And always she was aware of his warm gaze gliding over her. No longer was she embarrassed for him to catch her in the comfortable blue flannel caftan. Its fabric clung revealingly to her curves, as if molded to her slender shape by long years of use.

His dark liquid eyes twinkled as his gaze

took in her polished toes peeking below the robe's hem. "You don't like shoes, do you?"

She smiled sheepishly, her toes curling under. "Rarely does the weather here get cold enough to require shoes—so I grew up running barefooted. I was a wild child."

"I have the feeling that beneath that veneer of cosmopolitan classiness you still are a wild child."

"Is that bad?" she asked, disgusted with the coquettishness she heard in her voice.

He handed her the empty coffee cup. "I reckon that depends on what side of the tracks you come from. Me, I like it. I like everything about you."

Abruptly he swung away, as if he regretted saying as much as he had, and headed outside for the barn.

The calls to the sheriff's office were few and far between that day. Cassie had time to catch up on the back filing, departmental expense reports and the red tape of forms and copies that had to be filled out, in triplicate and quadruplicate in some instances. A batch of "Most Wanted" bulletins came in, and she perused the photos of the criminals' faces. Some of the faces looked like those of upstanding citizens—doctors, church leaders, businessmen. The kind one would never suspect.

Cade had been one of those criminals—the kind of man she would be foolish to trust.

She took lunch in the office, and Hernandez related the continuing saga of his efforts to

buy his fair Fatima from the Juarez brothel—
with installment payments, naturally.

When Cassie returned home that evening
she checked Grand Lady before cooking dinner. The mare was sweating over her shoulders and flanks and kicking at her abdomen.
Her time couldn't be too far off. Foaling was a
beautiful event; it made Cassie feel very close
to God, and she eagerly checked the mare
again after she had given Davey his bath and
tucked him into bed. Grand Lady was lying
down now and panting lightly.

"Easy, girl," Cassie whispered, stroking
the velvet soft muzzle. "It'll be over with
soon."

After she tied the mare's tail out of the way
with a gauze strip and hygienically cleaned
the posterior, she left the stall and slumped
down tiredly next to its wall. She folded her
legs before her, prepared to sit out the long
wait. Cade's gentle shaking of her shoulder
brought her head off her knees. "What time is
it?" she asked sleepily.

"Three-twenty. Dawn's not far off. I saw the
light when I drove in."

Where had he been until three in the morning? It was really none of her business, Cassie
reminded herself. She nodded over her shoulder at Grand Lady's stall. "It looks like the
mare's going to have a difficult delivery,
Cade."

His hand still rested on her shoulder. "I'll
spell you. Why don't you get some sleep?"

"Are you kidding—when I'm about to be a grandmother?"

He slid down next to her, his back propped against the pine-slatted wall. "You don't look old enough even to be a mother, Cass."

She smothered a yawn. "I feel very much like a mother tonight."

He pulled her into the crook of his arm, tipping her head against his solid shoulder. She offered no resistance. Instead she enjoyed the pleasant support his body afforded. Her lids closed in dreamy surrender, but snapped open when he said quietly, "Cass, tell me about your marriage."

"I—what do you want to know?" she asked cautiously, fully awake now.

"About the man . . . about his effect on you."

The need to tell someone of those lonely years had been weighing on her for a long time. Cade would be moving on one day—and he didn't run in the same circles she had—so she would have no worry about the sordid details of Mario's last years coming to light again to ruin Davey's life. Still she hesitated, not fully trusting Cade. When at last she spoke her words were cautiously picked and she was careful to generalize.

"My husband was a genius of a—an entertainer—who captivated every heart. Men's, women's and children's. A brilliant star in the night sky against which all other stars paled. He was incredibly handsome in a distinguished way, radiated charm, was intelligent without being a bore—every girl's dream of Prince Charming."

"What exactly did he do?"

"Oh, gave concerts, wrote words to songs, things like that."

Cade's fingers toyed with a rebellious lock of Cassie's hair. "Would I recognize any of them."

"No," she said a little too quickly. "It's not likely. They never made the pop charts."

"Go on."

"Falling in love with him was like living a fairy tale. Exactly. Because it wasn't real. His creative genius was buoyed by alcohol." She closed her lids against the flood of unwanted memories.

"And . . . ?" Cade prompted softly.

"I didn't discover his problem with alcohol until it was too late. Until the liquor store's bills began to mount. Until his charm faded along with the high after each drinking spree. We were like vagabonds those first few years, roaming Europe wherever his concerts took him. He had expensive tastes—I was brought up to work hard, live frugally.

"I went to work—against his wishes—in order to pay the bills. It seemed that my husband grew more dependent on alcohol—to the point where he wasn't even interested in his music or his career."

"Why did you stay?"

"Because I loved him," she said listlessly. "And I believed that love is forever."

"Do you still believe so?"

She didn't answer for a moment. "I suppose I'm still a romantic. Yes, I believe love lasts forever—but if either person changes, its composition changes."

"What happened after that?"

"We had been married about three years when I decided I wanted a child. I wanted to love someone who could respond to my love— and I unwisely hoped a child would stir my husband from his alcoholic apathy. It didn't. Instead his life-style seemed to become more decadent. . . ." She shuddered, recalling the party in their New York townhouse that she had walked in on one night.

"It wasn't too long before we discovered that he had developed cirrhosis of the liver. The doctors' bills, followed by the hospital's, soon soared beyond the liquor store's . . . until at last he was released from his misery."

"But not you?"

"I don't know, Cade. My mother's death . . . my husband's . . . those years after he died when I had to do a lot of traveling—they've intensified the need for permanence in my life—and in Davey's." She looked up at him, her lips curving in a sad half-smile. "Not for me the bright lights and fairy-tale heroes. I'll settle for a plain white house with roses all around it."

Cade kissed her upturned nose. "Want me to show you permanence?" He drew her to her feet and led her over to Grand Lady's stall. "Look, Cass. There's your permanence."

Grand Lady was stretched out on the bed of hay, pushing hard. A translucent sac appeared with a little hoof inside. Seconds later another foot and a muzzle quickly came into view. The mare pushed once more and the foal's entire body began to emerge. The whole process took less than twenty minutes. Within a few minutes more the mare was licking at the newborn filly's shiny coat. The filly, after several unsuccessful attempts, managed to get to her wobbly feet and find her mother's milk. The beautiful perfection in what Cassie witnessed never failed to renew her faith in the Omnipotent Father and abiding love.

Cade put his arm about her shoulders. "Let's go on back to the house, Widow Woman."

Chapter 6

THERE, SHE HEARD IT AGAIN. THE LOW MOAN.
Cassie sat up in bed, pushing her hair back
over her shoulder, and listened intently. Outside, a late May rain pattered against the
darkened windowpane. Had she heard the
sighing of the wind? When the restless moan
came again she pushed the sheets back and
padded into the hall. The wooden floor was
cool beneath her feet as she stood before
Davey's door. With a mother's concern she
strained to hear any irregularity in her son's
steady breathing.

Then her ears picked up the soft, keening
rasp once more. It came from her father's
room. Uncertainly she crossed to the doorway.
For once the light that Cade usually kept
burning late into the night was off. In the

stygian darkness her eyes focused on the patch of white sheet that rustled with each agitated movement of Cade's body. "Cade?" she whispered, worried that she would also wake Davey.

"No!" Cade groaned in what was almost a sob.

Quickly she went to stand at the side of his bed. The bare flesh of his upper torso was dusky against the sheets. His head tossed from one side to the other as his lips moved in smothered, panting moans. She leaned over the bed to touch his shoulder. It was damp with perspiration. "Cade," she said gently.

"No!" he cried aloud now. It was a wail that chilled the length of her spine. He bolted into a sitting position, his eyes wide, and grabbed at her wrists, jerking her down across him.

"Cade . . . Cade, it's Cassie," she whispered, truly frightened of the powerful man who crouched over her. His golden-eyed gaze was wild and incandescent in the darkness. His thumbs bit into the tender underside of her wrists. "Cade . . . please . . . let me go . . . you're hurting me."

He blinked, and she could see that sanity was restoring itself to his nightmare-darkened mind. His eyes were suspiciously moist. The pressure of his grip eased. "Cass," he ground out.

"You were dreaming . . . raving." Still pinned across his lap, she could smell the earthy male scent of his heated skin. The crisp hair that matted his stomach tickled her cheek. A pleasant stirring rippled through her. "Are you all right?" she breathed.

He released her wrists. "Yes. It was just an old dream."

His hands absently stroked her heavy hair back from her temple, his fingers raking the tangled skein of strands across the sheet that covered his thighs. It was an erotic action that she knew he was unaware of, yet its effect on her was cataclysmic. Her breath shortened. Her pulse quickened. She lay there, cradled in his lap. Beneath the sheets she knew he wore nothing. The knowledge aroused her. Her lids closed as she savored the exquisite sensations curling through her. Her wariness was forgotten in Cade's warm embrace . . . until a sixth sense alerted her that he, too, was slowly coming to feel that sensual current coursing between them.

His hand ceased its rhythmic stroking of her fleece white hair and slipped down to cup her cheek. "Cass." The one word was full of his wanting. The taut muscles beneath her told her of his need.

She pulled away. Her voice, when she found it, was raspy with the escalating turbulence that frayed her emotions. "If . . . you're all right . . . I'd better return to my bed."

In the darkness his hand touched her shoulder, bare but for the thin lacy strap of her gossamer nightgown, and detained her. "Stay." His voice was husky, the words a half command, half plea. "Only for a while. I don't want to go back to sleep just yet."

Against her better judgment she acquiesced and let him pull her down alongside him, his shoulder pillowing her head. Nightmares she could understand, though with Mario's death her own had ceased. But, then, perhaps it was because she no longer let herself slip into that deep sleep that invited them. "Do you want to tell me about the dream?"

"No . . . yes." He clasped her shoulder, his fingers worrying with her gown's strap as he talked, so softly sometimes that she had to strain to hear the tortured words.

"When the farms dried up during the years of the dust bowl, my father's parents lost their farm in Oklahoma. They had homesteaded the one hundred and sixty acres. For a small amount of taxes that they couldn't pay, that land was picked up by the banker who had foreclosed on them."

"Your parents must have been furious at such injustice," she murmured.

He shrugged. "It happened often—to many people—during those years. My father, who was in his late teens then, traveled with his parents to California. Like the hordes of other Okies, they were seeking work in California's fruit farms and grape vineyards. There my father met and fell in love with a beautiful young Mexican girl . . . my mother. They married. The migrant life became their way of life . . . my way of life."

For a moment Cade was silent, and she wondered if he was finished. Beneath her ear his pulse beat a hard rhythm that betrayed his agitation, as did the way the pad of his thumb softly whorled tantalizing circles into the flesh of her shoulder. He began speaking again. "When I was a child, I worked alongside my parents in the fields . . . sometimes hoeing, other times picking."

"And the child labor laws?" she said. "They weren't enforced, were they?"

His laugh was rueful. "Who would report a child? The growers? They only had to pay half the wages they would to an adult. My parents? We needed the money to eat."

She knew that some growers in Hidalgo County still turned their backs on this practice, though it was difficult to prove they did so. In some states the growers commanded strong police support and faithful obedience from the local judiciary. Citizens kowtowed to the growers' authority because they stood to lose if they sided with the migrant farm workers, who offered no tax base.

"After my brother was born I babysat him in the old car my parents would park alongside the fields. When Billy began to crawl I would entertain him . . . usually in the shade of a tree."

Cade's fingers halted their fretful stroking to tightly grasp her shoulder. "One day . . . so quickly I don't know how it happened . . . I

turned around, and he was gone. He had
toddled away. I searched the high grass and
shrubbery . . . couldn't find him . . . started
to run . . ."

Perspiration beaded now across Cade's burnished flesh. His breathing was ragged. "The
irrigation ditches . . . My father found him,
drowned."

"Cade," she murmured. There was nothing
else to be said. She brushed away the perspiration that sheened his throbbing jaw.

The agony left his voice to be replaced by a
dead, neutral tone. "Migrant life taught me to
sleep cramped . . . to eat standing . . . to
block my mind against the bitter cold and
blistering heat . . . to be prepared for the ridi-
cule with each new school I attended . . . to
never make the mistake of getting attached to
a lot of places and possessions. And people."

She knew that what she was about to do
could harm the delicate balance that existed
in the household between her and Cade, but
she sensed the enormity of his emotional need
—made worse because he was such a private,
isolated individual. She rose up on one elbow
and, hand splayed across his chest for support, leaned over to kiss him. There was nothing passionate or sensual in her kiss. Rather it
was an outpouring of comfort, replacing
words that could not be spoken.

He lay there, his lips motionless against her
softly moving ones. She kissed each end of his

mouth, nudged his lower lip with her top one, then dropped down to graze the indentation in his chin with the tip of her tongue.

Abruptly his hands captured her shoulders; his mouth imprisoned hers. It began as a brutal kiss, as if he would turn the guilt and pain of his past on her. Then, subtly, the kiss changed, evolved, giving pleasure as hers had given comfort.

Years . . . it had been years since she had been kissed—if she ever had been the way Cade Montoya was kissing her now. He kissed her with a gentleness she had never experienced. His lips traced soft patterns over her cheeks as he murmured his need of her.

"Cass . . . you're always on my mind. . . ." His mouth reclaimed hers, his tongue parting her lips. Involuntarily she responded to that kiss. Tilting her head, she matched her lips to his, her tongue seeking to join with its counterpart. His hand slid inside the nightgown's bodice to cup the underswell of one breast, and her breath rasped with the thrill of his touch.

"Your body is beautiful, Cass. . . . I lie here awake at night, wondering what it would be like to touch your skin . . . if it's as satiny smooth as it looks. I've thought about going to your room . . . knowing what I wanted would be near-rape . . . that I had no right. . . ." His thumb and forefinger found her nipple, taut with the desire his kisses, his words, his touch were building in her. "Your breasts—childbearing hasn't marred them . . . firm, supple . . . full."

She felt that she was losing all grip on reality. A tomorrow would come when Cade would be gone. It was sheer folly to let this happen. "Cade . . ." But her protest died with the pleasurable pressure he exerted on her nipple.

He rolled over her so that his thigh sprawled across the lower half of her body. His nakedness set her afire. Her hands slid around his waist and upward to clutch at his brawny shoulders. Never had she wanted a man as she did this man—this stranger—who held her and kissed her with a wild lust that imparted itself to her.

"Nurture me, Cass," he whispered, his tongue tracing the brown areola of one nipple that had wrinkled with her own need.

Her back arched as she cupped her breast to lift it to his mouth. His jaws flexed as he took the nipple between his teeth and gently sucked. "Cade . . . Cade . . . please . . . Cade." The words were an incoherent litany trilling from her parted lips.

His hand caught the hem of her gown and pushed it up over her thighs. His fingers pushed aside her panties, and her legs spread in mindless abandon. He touched her—bonded her to him with that touch. She gasped as a fiery wave of unsustainable pleasure crashed over her. Her rapid breathing reverberated in her ears.

And then another sound reached her. That of Davey's sleepy call. "Mama."

She stiffened. What was she doing? Giving herself to a stranger . . . a man who was only passing through. She had to be half out of her mind. Half out of her mind with the need he had generated in her.

Davey called again, the call of a child who wasn't fully awake. This time Cade lifted his head. In the darkness his amber eyes burned brightly with passion, but his voice was controlled, concerned. "Your son. Davey needs you, Cass." He rolled off her, pulling her nightgown strap up over her shoulder. "Go to him. Children shouldn't wake up alone."

She rose, still weak with the force of the desire that had lapped against her, battering her like a tidal wave. She smoothed the gown down over her hips, preparing what she had to say, before glancing up to meet the hot gaze that branded her flesh, making her his.

He sat before her, one arm propped on a hooked knee, unashamed of the bold masculinity he displayed. "Cass, come back . . . later, when Davey's settled."

She shook her head, and her hair fell in a swath across one eye. "I can't—"

Davey's call, more plaintive now, interrupted her. She swung away from Cade and hurried to her son's room. She would have to talk

with Cade. He would have to go. He couldn't
stay there after what had happened between
the two of them.

Cade wiped the back of his arm across his
sweat-filmed forehead. Flexing his arms out-
ward, he arched his back to ease the kinks
that came from hunching over the prehistoric
tractor on which he was working. The heavy
ridges of muscles in his shoulders protested at
the recent weeks of hard physical labor after
years of disuse. He needed to be swinging an
axe again.

He needed to be gone from the Duval ranch.
Staying on could only mean trouble. It
would mean involvement. And involvement
would mean a difficult, painful situation
when the time came to leave, to move on. And
that time would come. It always did. He had
left friends and foes scattered across the face
of the earth. Their visages occasionally returned to jangle his thoughts. . . .

The sinister white-bearded Indian guru who
had mesmerized foreigners and bilked them
of their fortunes, intriguing Cade enough that
he spent three months interviewing the man.
Regina, the Peace Corps worker who had
given him the inside info on Nigeria's mania-
cal dictator and, in the process, given Cade
her heart. The saintly-looking Connecticut
doctor who had cold-bloodedly administered a
lethal injection of potassium chloride to his

socialite wife. Caroline, whose devoted work in the Appalachians for the Frontier Nursing Service had sparked an idea in him for another book—and whose divine lovemaking had kept him in the hills days beyond his deadline.

And there were others, gentle people like Armadeo, whose names would never be renowned, but whose courage to face the daily vicissitudes that beset them drew greater admiration from him than all the feats and good deeds of the media-hyped public figures.

Once more he hunkered down beside the old Ford tractor, half cursing the in-depth research technique that had earned him high acclaim for his accurately-depicted nonfiction books that read like novels. That same technique required that he know his subjects—the people he portrayed—thoroughly. Unscrupulous men like Jonathan Reinhart . . . and spirited women like Cassie Garolini.

But the latter wasn't entirely true. . . . There was no other woman like Cass. Mysterious, warm, aloof, passionate, giving, intelligent, beautiful—never had he encountered one woman who was all these things to him. He ached to possess her. But he didn't believe in possessing anything. How then could he end this need of her?

Seeing her and not touching her . . . watching the soft sway of her breasts and the tantalizing movement of her hips when she walked . . . catching her woman's earthy fresh scent some mornings before she added perfume . . . listening to her mellifluous speech when she talked with Davey. Every day was torture for him.

The night when she had come to his bedroom—after the horror of the nightmare had ebbed—he had imperceptibly grown aware of the flame of desire that smoldered in her eyes. With an animal's instinct he had scented the subtle woman's odor that was sparked by deep sexual arousal. Her heightened sensuality had been almost tangible in the smoky aura that had emanated from her.

He had lost all vestiges of control then and kissed her. In that one kiss he had felt all the emotions—shock, resistance, uncertainty, and finally that ember of passion—one succeeding the other, that had coursed through the pliant body that contrasted so with her unyielding nature. And what he had felt—it had staggered him.

If he ever again permitted himself to succumb to that white-hot electrical current that sizzled between them—if he ever made love to her—they would both be lost. When the time came to move on the pain of leaving would wrench his gut. And what harm would it do to her and Davey?

Was love finally catching up with him? If so, it was too late. He was too old. Thirty-seven was too old to change the only way of life he had ever known. He couldn't make compromises; he couldn't settle down. . . . A claustrophobic net always descended over him when he spent too long a time in one place.

Cell fever was what the politician had called it. The man had been a prominent Washington figure caught in a nationwide scandal, and Cade, doing time in the same penitentiary for his part in a nuclear waste protest march, had wrangled enough material from the man for another bestseller.

He gave the wrench a vicious jerk and pinched the webbing between his thumb and forefinger in the top link. A curse escaped from between his clenched teeth, and he jammed his throbbing hand beneath his armpit.

"Tsk-tsk," Cassie said behind him.

His head swiveled upward, his disgusted gaze clashing with her amused one. Dressed in denim cutoffs and a white cotton shirt knotted at her slender waist, she was breathtaking. The hard core of desire reawoke. Even as his eyes took in her long, slender legs, he noted that the flesh in the valley of her breasts was gleaming with perspiration. She had been jogging again.

"It hurt," he growled plaintively.

She smiled, and he felt like he had just had a sunstroke. "You sound like Davey." She held out a beer can frosted with rivulets of condensation. "Will this help?"

"Lady, you can't imagine how much that will help," he said and, surprising her, dropped a quick kiss on each of her dusty shoes. "Thank you, thank you."

She stepped backward a pace, a peculiar expression on her face. He pretended that he hadn't seen the expression and accepted the can she passed him, asking, "You're not partaking?"

"Beer blows the diet," she murmured.

The can was deliciously cold in his hand and only slightly chillier than the look that suddenly frosted her eyes. He caught that look, fixed on his bare chest, before she hastily lifted her gaze to his face. And he understood then the reason for that look—wariness, perhaps even self-disgust at her susceptibility to him. Whatever the reason for it, the look was quickly camouflaged by one of polite formality.

She was right, of course. It would be much wiser to maintain a formal distance between them during the rest of his stay in Lordsburg. He took her cue and, rising to his feet, said, "You have something you need me to do?"

She wandered toward the front of the tractor, presenting her delectable bottom for his perusal. The scorching sun beat down on his back, and his need of her pulsed in his brain and body.

Her fingers trailed aimlessly across the tractor's side panel, furrowing its coat of dust. "The other night—I—it was an indiscretion on my part."

He could only admire her honesty in assuming responsibility for her part in what had happened that night. But he knew that she had something else to say. He leaned a greasy forearm against the tractor's fender. "Oh?"

She spun about. "It can't—won't—happen again!"

He didn't believe her, of course. What had happened between them was too hot, too elemental, to be denied. If he stayed long enough, their passion would explode, hurting them and everyone around them. But he said nothing, setting his face in an expressionless mold.

Yet he could tell by the way her fist clenched, the way her perfect, white teeth bit at her lower lip, that his silence seemed to her to refute her statement. She wanted some reassuring word from him. She wanted—needed—his cooperation. Using the beer to buy time, he tilted the can to his mouth while his mind rifled through the various replies he could make—and rejected them all in favor of the simplicity of the truth.

He wiped his mouth with the back of his hand and set the can on the tractor seat. He shifted his weight to one leg and faced her, planting his hands at his hips. "Cass, I want you badly—you're a woman I could easily fall in love with. Maybe I already am. But there's a part of me that's restive. Some day I'd have to move along. It would hurt us both. And the last thing I want to do is hurt you."

He could see that his words stung her pride.

Her chin lifted willfully. "Then since we both agree on the importance of . . . of suppressing certain emotions, we shouldn't have any problem maintaining an employer/employee relationship, should we?"

He thrust his hands into the back pockets of his jeans to keep them from reaching out and pulling her to him. His fingers ached to feel the heaviness of her breasts again, to cup the delightful curve of her buttocks. "We shouldn't," he echoed, desperately wanting to believe it.

Chapter 7

SUNLIGHT FROM THE CHURCH'S HIGH stained-glass window filtered down to halo Cassie's bowed head, making the summer white mane that cascaded down her back look like the spun angel hair of Christmas. But it was June and already scorching that early Sunday morning. Against the heat Cassie wore a white linen suit with an apricot silk blouse.

Next to her Davey sat, doodling on the offering envelope while the minister delivered the doxology. Several rows ahead sat Miss Creighburg, and a row over she could see Jonathan Reinhart and his son, the pillars of the community.

When the services were over Marilyn and Curly joined Cassie and Davey in the aisle.

"Why don't you come over for dinner this afternoon?" Marilyn asked. "You stay so busy, we never get to see you two."

"I'd love to, Marilyn, but I've got to keep an eye on a mare that's colicky."

"Isn't that your hired hand?" Curly asked. "There, at the doorway, talking to the reverend."

Cassie's glance swerved in the direction Curly indicated. Bright sunlight fanned through the open double doors. The minister's whooping-crane figure was silhouetted beside Cade's taller, more powerful physique. She recalled the day when he had appeared in the barn's doorway. Her analogy then had been accurate: He was a dark angel.

"Cade could come, too," Marilyn added with that matchmaker light in her eye again. But the light faded, and she touched Cassie's arm, saying in a lowered voice, "Cassie, he is attractive in a dangerous sort of way . . . a convict and all that . . . but my income, unlike yours, doesn't depend on public opinion. Do be careful."

Cassie nodded distractedly. How did one turn off an attraction? She only wished that she could, that it could be as easy as flipping off a light.

The congregation pressed forward to shake the minister's hand, and she found herself standing not far from Cade when her time came to offer her hand to the minister. He pressed it warmly and uttered some polite comment, but she was barely listening. She was too aware of Cade at her side.

More than a week had passed since that afternoon when she had taken him the can of beer. Since then he had been impeccably polite, though she detected in his expressive eyes and mobile lips an amusement at their situation. Irrationally, she missed the occasional bantering she had enjoyed with him.

But, as Marilyn had pointed out, keeping Cade on at the ranch was causing talk that could harm her chances for election come November. Yet there was the dilemma of finding other help. Who would work for bed and board alone? Reliable help—with any knowledge of horses—would want some kind of wages.

Between the wages of a hired hand and the money she paid Anaberta to care for Davey, there would be little money left to keep the ranch going. A catch-22, it seemed. But something had to be done. Cade Montoya had invaded her house, then her thoughts, and now . . . now her dreams. She blushed, remembering the sexual fantasy she had dreamed about Cade the night before.

"I'm sorry, Reverend," she murmured, abashed that she hadn't been paying attention to the minister's words. "I didn't catch what you were saying."

"I was just expressing my gratitude, Sheriff, for the visitor you have introduced into our congregation." He nodded toward Cade, who lazed against the door, hands in his jeans pockets. His one concession to the religious services was a tweed jacket worn over his tieless white shirt that was open at the neck.

He straightened and cast her a smile that electrified her nerve endings. How silly at her age to lose her self-containment over a man— and a convict, at that. "I was just telling the reverend here of some impoverished migrant families the church could visit, Cass."

"Our members will be glad to help the people out, Mr. Montoya," the minister said.

"Thank you, Reverend." Cade flicked an impersonal glance at Cass. "Any chance you could give me a lift back? I've lent my car to Armadeo—his mother is ill in Hermosillo, down in Mexico."

"Of course," she replied with cool formality, though she really wanted to refuse.

Davey latched on to Cade's hand. "Have you finished the duck pond yet, Cade?"

Cade glanced down and ruffled the boy's cotton candy hair. "It's coming along, son."

Cassie's lips flattened. That made everything just dandy. . . . Now Cade had beguiled Davey, also.

Cade clasped her arm and steered her toward the four-wheeler parked beneath the shade of the twisted giant cottonwood. It was the heat of the day, and yet goose bumps of excitement broke out all over her flesh. Just his touch . . . What in heaven's name was she going to do about her predicament?

"Sheriff!"

Cassie turned to find Miss Creighburg coming toward her. The black plume on the woman's hat, standing out against the background of the white clapboard church, fluttered with each step she took. She poked her cane indignantly at Cade and Cassie. "What's Lordsburg coming to when God-fearing people have to attend church with—with fornicators!"

Cassie gasped.

A few people nearby overheard Miss Creighburg's denunciation and turned to look. Cassie's face burned with shame, but her fury was greatest that the woman would attack her in front of Davey. She started to shake, but Cade's firm-yet-warning grip at her elbow both steadied her and silenced the irate words that trembled on her lips.

He turned the full power of his devastating charm on the old lady. "I do believe, Miss Creighburg, that our Father forgives all, so why don't we all behave in the same spirit?"

"Really!" the matriarch drawled with a fulminating glance that would have shriveled the skin off a snake before she stalked away from the couple and the little boy who was protectively wedged between them.

Cassie felt sick to her stomach. Then Davey asked, "Mama, what's a fornicator?"

"A what?"

"It's just a word," Cade said, and propelled her and Davey to the passenger side of the car before the boy could ask any more questions. "I'll drive," he said.

Once the churchyard faded behind them she blurted, "How could you, Cade? What you told Miss Creighburg—it was as much as admitting that . . . that something was going on between us!"

She saw him glance in the rearview mirror at Davey, who sat in the back seat. "Not now, Cass."

She tilted her head back and closed her eyes, wishing she could block out the ugly scene at the church. "What must everyone think?" she muttered.

"Good God, Cass! She's only one vituperative woman. Why don't you let Lordsburg's citizens decide who's righteous enough to cast the first stone?"

Later, as she chopped the onions for the Sunday dinner meatloaf, she agonized over her dilemma. She could ask Cade—no, damn it, tell him; it was after all her home—to fix a place for himself in the barn. But what good would his sleeping in the barn accomplish? People would believe what they wanted, that she and Cade were having an affair.

The trouble was that he had made himself indispensable about the ranch. Even now—on Sunday, his day off—he was climbing the windmill's tower to affix the blade he had ordered.

It was unfortunate that the HCFWA didn't

demand more of his time, but right now
Reinhart was working fields that were inac-
cessible to the pickets' urging shouts. All was
seemingly peaceful—for the moment. Cade,
so Anaberta told her, was presently involved
in organizing a statewide boycott of Reinhart
chiles. It seemed that Anaberta and everyone
else in Lordsburg knew all about Cade's activ-
ities, when she didn't even know what time
he might come home at night.

But his plans for organizing a boycott explained the radio station van that she had
seen parked in front of the HCFWA headquarters. He was apparently going to use the mass
media to apply pressure on the large growers.

The onions brought tears streaming down
her face, and Davey paused in building his
house of playing cards to ask, "Are you crying,
Mama?"

"No." But she wanted to. "It's just the
onions that are causing these tears, pet."

She cracked an egg over the bowl and viciously beat it into the hamburger meat. Until
she could find a replacement for Cade, she
would just have to avoid him as much as
possible—which was rather difficult when she
had to sit across the dinner table from him,
feeling the heat of his gaze burning over her
or when an ill horse or setting a fence post
required the two of them to work alongside
each other or when she washed his sheets,
still faintly scented with his shaving lotion.

While Davey chattered at dinner she was decidedly distant and quite relieved that the windmill would require Cade's attention for the rest of the day. That night in bed she studied the U. S. Department of Justice's *Jail Resource Manual* for the forthcoming mini-course at the Law Enforcement Academy, hoping that it would distract her from the slit of light beneath Cade's doorway.

Was he reading also—or thinking the same tantalizing thoughts as she?

"Sheriff," said a voice, as gravelly as a cement mixer, at the other end of the phone. "Jonathan Reinhart here."

With an inaudible groan she closed her eyes and pushed back a stray lock of hair. Old man Reinhart rarely made personal calls; usually his son Eric or the farm's battery of corporate lawyers acted as his task force and handled any unpleasant problems. But apparently this time the old man felt that the situation called for his own persuasive pressure, which was quite influential considering the fact that he kept a Machiavellian finger in many pots: the state labor board, the railroad commission, board seats in several prominent New Mexico banks. A quick executionary flick of his finger brought low those who dared to oppose him in any way.

"Yes?" she replied carefully, waiting for the axe to fall.

"My son tells me Reinhart Farms is suffering a slight drop in productivity due to certain labor disputes."

So? "Yes?"

"You've checked into the matter?"

He knew damned well that she had been out to the fields. His intelligence network, managed by the fat roach Rico, reported everything that affected Reinhart Farms in any way, ranging from a single bruised chile to which of the pickers was sleeping with whom. "I've driven by your fields."

"Now, Sheriff . . ." Jonathan Reinhart's voice softened to a gentle tone that a minister would have envied. She was not deceived. She knew what was coming. "This is a problem that I know you can handle. Why don't we discuss it—say, over dinner Friday night."

It was not an invitation but a summons. Still, she would not be intimidated so easily. "I think you should talk over your . . . problem . . . with the people responsible for your drop in productivity," she said silkily. "The Hidalgo County Farm Workers Association."

"An excellent suggestion. I'll expect you and Cade Montoya for dinner Friday."

The phone went dead in her hands. She stared at it as if it were a scorpion. Damn!

She was furious with Cade. The mess she was in was of his making. She dialed his headquarters. Ramona reported in her lioness's purring voice that Cade was not in.

Cassie banged the receiver down and called out to Hernandez that she was heading for Reinhart Farms.

As she suspected, Cade was in Reinhart's fifth sector. It bordered the service road and had yet to be sprayed with insecticide. She passed by a string of parked pickups and cars that looked ready for the scrapyard and pulled in alongside his old station wagon. His lieutenants surrounded him, listening as he talked. She sat in her car, waiting for him to finish and feeling slightly guilty, as if she were eavesdropping.

Cade's lieutenants were for the most part women—the young and the ancient, the toil-worn and the freshly beautiful, the rotund and the skeletal. But in all their eyes glimmered the same spark of hope, generated by the encouraging words of the man who spoke in quiet but firm tones. Hands planted on his hips, he made no gestures; rather he let simple but expressive words, pauses, eye contact and inflection accomplish his purpose. At times his features were darkly beautiful . . . at other times he was almost ugly. Like the lieutenants, Cassie sat mesmerized until he finished. The spell broken, the workers dispersed like ants on a foraging mission.

When he crossed to her car she schooled her face to an impassive expression, concealing the tumultuous emotions that churned inside her. He leaned on the window and said in that rough, rich voice that seemed to stroke her soul, "Did anyone ever tell you that dressed in those white jeans and hat you look like that sexy cowgirl in those shampoo commercials?"

Despite her intention to maintain a stern demeanor she had to smile, because she was acquainted with the beautiful young woman who did those commercials. Initially Cassie had been requested for the assignment, but at that time she had been on location in Rome, shooting an ad for a major perfume company.

"What was that about?" she asked, nodding toward the cars driving away.

He grinned. "A lesson in scare tactics."

"From a man who declares that his policy is nonviolence, I find that statement difficult to accept."

"Mostly I covered the 'don'ts' that will keep the pickets from getting arrested by our local sheriff." It was gentle mockery, and she knew that no response was expected. "This field is next in line to be worked," he continued, "and I want the picketing to go smoothly. Reinhart would be devious enough to work the pickers at night to avoid our pickets if he thought he could get away with it."

The mention of Reinhart reminded her of her reason for driving out, but out of curiosity she delayed that subject for the moment. "Your lieutenants, Cade—why so many women?"

His eyes searched her face, as if he weren't certain how seriously he should answer the question. "I've learned that women have something very special, Cass—staying power. With men it's always we *want* it, let's *do* it. We want to finish it up in seconds. But women just keep going. If a man is full of machismo, he can't appreciate what women do. But if he's not . . . well, it's really something beautiful."

His philosophy stunned her. Never would she have expected a statement like that from a man of such obvious masculine attributes. Usually that sort of philosophy was spouted by effete men with pseudointellectual leanings. It also frightened her just a little that he could so easily delve into the psyche of the opposite sex.

"Your female pickets are going to need that staying power, Cade. Jonathan Reinhart called me this afternoon. He's the most influ—"

"I know all about him. I made it my business to know before I ever made the decision to come to Lordsburg and organize a laborers' association."

"Then I don't have to tell you he's losing patience. He's set up a command performance for the two of us for dinner at his house this Friday."

"Good. When the growers refuse to sit down at the bargaining table, there's no alternative but to strike. Perhaps we can persuade Reinhart that a few simple compromises would make both sides more cooperative."

She raised a brow. "We?"

His grin was lopsided and terribly appealing. "For sure, Widow Woman. We seem to be making quite a team—if Miss Creighburg's opinion is any indication."

"Wow, Mama!" Davey issued an imitation wolf whistle from between the narrow gap in his two front teeth. "You look bad!"

Cassie smiled down at her son and stooped to give him a kiss. "I take it that's good?"

"For sure!"

And that was an imitation of Cade, Cassie thought with a sigh of hopelessness. "Go along with you, Davey," she said with a loving swat on his behind.

Straightening, she finished knotting the long wrappy scarf at the base of the rose-hued poet blouse. She gave the antique pier mirror a glance, turning about to view herself from the rear. No, the raspberry jersey skirt didn't cling unflatteringly to her hips. Rather its soft, flowing fabric subtly accented her curves.

Modeling had at least taught her that much —that with selective coordination of natural fibers, subdued shades for her personal skin tone, a fabric's sheen and drape for her particular figure—she could achieve a chic wardrobe on a limited budget.

The digital alarm clock on her nightstand warned her that she and Cade were due at Reinhart's in less than thirty minutes, and

she would have to drop Davey off at
Anaberta's first. Hastily she caught her hair
at her nape to pin it up in its usual artful knot.
"Don't," Cade said negligently from the doorway.

She pivoted. Arms crossed, he leaned
against the doorjamb. With his tan slacks he
wore a camel corduroy jacket that highlighted
his bronze coloring. His yellowish hazel eyes,
fringed with curling sable lashes, picked up
the hue of the jacket. His overpowering virility set her heart fluttering against her ribs like
a bird futilely beating its wings against its
cage. The fact that his nose had been broken,
that his grin was lopsided, his teeth slightly
irregular—all combined to make his charm
irresistible.

"What did you say?" she asked in a breathless voice.

"Your hair—leave it down."

"Why?"

His hands made a man's helpless gesture.
"You know what I mean, Cass—all sleek,
smooth, hanging down your back."

She smiled. "That's the first time I've heard
you be less than articulate, Cade Montoya."

Watching his reaction, she shook her head
in a seductive manner, loosening her hair
until it swung free in a sun-bleached cascade.
"Is this what you wanted?" she asked, her
voice brimming with feminine guile.

"It'll do for a start," he growled.

As they drove to Anaberta's, Cassie wondered if Davey, seated between Cade and her, could sense the sexual tension that seemed to permeate the air in the station wagon. After Davey got out she was careful to keep to the far side of the seat and stare out the window, as if she found the flat desert landscape of tremendous interest.

When Cade swung the car off onto the private road leading to Reinhart's estate the landscape was transformed into something more like the Babylonian Gardens. Tall, stately date palms, interspersed with fragrant, flowering jacaranda and oleander, flanked the long drive up to the bright white two-story stucco home built in the territorial style. Black wrought-iron balustrades, laced with brilliant red bougainvillea, ran the length of the upper and lower verandas. A lava-stone fountain that spilled with sparkling water was the focal point of the circular drive.

Though Cassie had lived in Lordsburg most of her life, she had never seen the home, only heard descriptions. "Quite a contrast to the camps old Reinhart provides for his workers, isn't it?" Cade said.

"At least he provides housing for them. Some growers don't, as you doubtlessly already know." Why was she defending a man she barely knew and doubted she could even like?

Cade's hard gaze left the road to fix on her tight-lipped profile. "You call corrugated tin shacks, without electricity or running water, housing?"

Silence reigned until a Mexican-American boy in a loose white cotton *camisa* and *calzones* answered their knock on the massive hand-carved double doors. Eric, looking magnificently handsome in an indigo polo shirt and matching trousers, entered the adobe-tiled foyer. "Cassie." He greeted her with an engaging smile. "It's about time. After ten years I've finally wrangled your presence at our dinner table."

His smile congealed as he turned to Cade. "And it would seem, Mr. Montoya, that you are our nemesis."

Cade shook the hand Eric proffered. "Think of me more as your conscience, Reinhart."

Eric ignored the barb and informed them that his father would join them shortly. A plushly carpeted and mahogany-paneled den contained the bar facilities, where Eric poured California wine for the three of them. Seated on deeply tufted leather chairs, they talked cursorily of the chile rot, the new municipal pool, the continuing war in the Middle East and its effects on the national economy.

At that point old man Reinhart entered the room. He was a powerful, volatile man with a high forehead and bull-like shoulders. Fierce, grizzled eyebrows were pinched in over his hooded eyes. Custom demanded that once again a polite exchange of amenities be conducted—more talk of the weather, a brief tour of the house, and several more glasses of wine at dinner—before the slightest hint of business was allowed to enter the conversation.

"You understand our position, Mr. Montoya," Jonathan Reinhart said smoothly. "If we increase wages, it will put the product out of reach of the consumer—which will help neither the picker nor the grower."

Cade twirled his wineglass idly. "Cesar Chavez proved to the California grape growers that that wasn't a valid argument."

"What the hell can we do," Eric interrupted, "when the government won't give us price support for our crops like it does other industries? We've no choice but to budget with low labor cost."

"Eric," his father reproved firmly. "Mr. Montoya, I would like to point out that our New Mexico farm workers enjoy higher wages than those in most other states."

"But not protective laws, Reinhart." Cade leaned forward, and Cassie knew that this was the brunt of his demands. "We have pickers who have been knocked unconscious by the poisonous insecticides the dusting rigs spray. Why aren't they provided with spray suits—masks—gloves?"

Jonathan Reinhart slammed his hand on the dining table. "Because it cost money that the grower can't afford!"

Cade's brows rose in mock wonderment.

"You mean this house is of more value than children who have suffered blindness and death because of exposure to pesticides?"

Reinhart's wrinkled eyelids slid over his piercing eyes so that he looked like some reptilian monster that had roamed the Pyramid Valley eons before, when it had been partially under water. His voice lowered to a scaly rasp. His words were precise—deliberate. "I'm going to break you open like a shotgun before this is over, Mr. Montoya. And you, Sheriff—I'd advise you to walk a very narrow path."

Chapter 8

HERNANDEZ DROPPED THE SUBPOENA ON Cassie's desk, and she arched a questioning brow.

"That speeding ticket you gave the guy from Texas—you gotta testify."

"That's just great," she muttered. "When? In my spare time?"

Hernandez's pink cheeks dimpled in a grin. "The fire chief is waiting to see you about tickets to their Fourth of July picnic."

"Tell him I'm going to be out of town." Which was true, since she would be in Santa Fe that week, attending the Law Enforcement Academy.

"And Cade Montoya called."

"Tell him—no, what did he want?"

"Says he wants you to come by the HCFWA

this afternoon—when you get a chance, he says."

A resigned smile curved her lips. "When I get a chance, of course."

"Of course," Hernandez repeated, his grin larger, his leprechaun's dimples deeper.

In spite of her sang-froid before Hernandez, her blood pressure was soaring, then diving like a sail plane out of control when she parked before the HCFWA headquarters. Several days had gone by since the dinner at Reinhart's, and she and Cade had seen each other only in passing, usually over hastily swallowed cups of coffee in the morning. They tiptoed around as if the other were mined with TNT. The situation was indeed becoming explosive in that sexually-charged atmosphere.

But she didn't know how to solve the problem, much less cope with the new feelings of heightened sensuality that assailed her. Never, in all the years she had been glorified as the ultimate in femininity and womanhood, had she ever felt so much a woman as she did when she was with Cade. Yet nothing good, nothing permanent could come of that relationship. She couldn't afford to let herself go, to let her feelings have free rein. The day would come when the price would be too high to pay.

As usual, the screen door squeaked on its warped hinges when she entered, and dust particles flurried in the shaft of sunlight.

Another desk had been added to the outer office, and Armadeo sat behind it, deep in conversation on the telephone. Where before a paltry number of farm workers had wandered in and out of the offices, a score or more crowded the room, waiting to see Cade about insurance, social services, complaints and who knew what else. The office hummed with people talking in English, Spanish and the curious combination of the two that was called Tex-Mex.

Cade was bent over Ramona's shoulder, scratching out something in a letter before them on the desk. He wore a green fatigue shirt that did nothing to soften his rough-hewn features.

He looked up at Cassie, and the smile he gave was grim. "Come on back to my office, Cass."

He closed the door behind her, muttering, "Ramona can't take shorthand worth a damn, but she sure can placate disgruntled union members."

"I just bet." He cast her an exasperated look, and she said, "You needed to see me?"

He leaned back in his swivel chair and crossed his hands behind his head. "The HCFWA wants to file a complaint on Rico."

Obviously this wasn't going to be a short conversation. She slid into a vinyl-covered chair, the seat of which was punctured by a spring. "For what?"

"He intentionally backed the Reinhart farm

truck into one of our pickets—Robles—and knocked him down."

"Is Robles hurt?"

"He's at the clinic now. Broken arm, maybe. But his anger is what needs to be treated—legally, if we can. Otherwise he'll get mad enough one day to take the law into his own hands—and then you'll have a real problem, Cass."

Absently her forefinger played with the indentation in the center of her lower lip while she pondered the possible repercussions. "You realize that proving Rico intentionally ran down Robles will be difficult. It will involve a lengthy court case—and will be costly."

Cade shrugged. "The AFL-CIO's lawyers have volunteered to handle the cost. Normally I don't like to take donations from outside organizations, because the people who give the money can tell you how to use it. But this time the money will go to a specific purpose."

This was the ruthless side of Cade. Cassie had known that it had to exist for him to possess the leadership qualities he did, but this was the first time she had seen the ruthlessness in action. When she said nothing he leaned forward. "Cass, there's no such thing as riding the fence. If you're not for something, then you're automatically cast against it. Whose side are you on?"

"I'm on the side of right and justice," she snapped, and stood up. "And which side that is is decided by the courts."

He grinned, and she realized that he had trapped her. "Good. Then take my sworn statement."

Angry that she had been so easily conned, she said, "See Hernandez. He'll handle your paperwork."

She turned and stalked to the door, but before she could open it he said, "Cass—could the HCFWA use the P.A. system under the hood of your Charger? We need it to reach the workers in the further fields."

She flashed him a blistering look and slammed the door behind her.

Rhythmically Cade swung the shovel. He wore no shirt, and sweat ran in rivulets down his skin. Cassie, leaning against the veranda's cedar post, covertly watched the play of the bronzed skin across his back. Even the corded muscles in his taut stomach, when his arms swung upward, rippled beneath his flesh.

In the scorching heat the jacarandas scented the veranda with their sultry fragrance. It was siesta time in that part of the country, yet Cade worked steadily. Cassie couldn't take her eyes off him. When he paused to shove back his sweat-dampened curls with the crook of his arm, his gaze locked with hers. A flush of heat, which had nothing to do with the soaring temperature of the summer afternoon, flooded her face. Cade couldn't have failed to see the undisguised admiration in her eyes. With an assumed nonchalance she left the veranda to saunter across the yard toward him. Pee Wee automatically rose from his position at her feet and followed behind her.

"Lunch is about ready, Cade."

His chest rose and fell with the exertion of his work. "Fine," he said after a moment.

She searched for something to say. "How's the duck pond coming?" A silly, empty question.

He propped a boot on the spade and braced an arm on the handle. "The trench should be finished by tomorrow, and then we can open the irrigation gate and let the water through to the pond."

Without thinking she reached out to wipe at the stream of sweat that coursed down the center of his ribcage. He caught her hand and held it in his callused one. For a naked moment their eyes communicated the wanting that their lips refused to acknowledge with words.

There was nothing to say—or else there was everything to say. He released her hand. She turned to go, and as though seeking to detain her, he asked, "Rico—what's happened on the sworn statement I filed?"

"I turned the statement over to the district attorney's office yesterday. It will be up to him to decide if the case is worth pursuing."

No doubt Eric and his father were far from pleased about Cade's intent to prosecute. But she had only carried out an obligation of the sheriff's office and could incur no rebuke from Lordsburg's most prominent citizens.

Cade nodded and hunkered down to scratch Pee Wee between the ears. The dog's tail thumped ecstatically against the sun-baked earth. "You know, I never had a dog. I always wanted one, but my father said we moved around too much." He looked up at her, his gaze burning into hers. "He was right, of course. I would have become too attached. . . . If the dog had run away or gotten lost . . . well, it breaks a child's heart, doesn't it?"

She understood the message. "It breaks anyone's heart," she said in a toneless voice and turned away.

As she walked back to the house Pee Wee traitorously remained at Cade's side. Davey was just as traitorous later over the light lunch of ham sandwiches and chips. His attention was wholly centered on Cade. "When can we get the ducks? Do we need baby ducks?"

Cade gave him a tolerant smile. "The mama and daddy ducks will take care of that for us, son."

He fastened his amused gaze on Cassie, and she concentrated on swallowing the lemonade left in her glass so that she wouldn't laugh.

"Speaking of mamas and daddies, Cass—if you have time this afternoon, I thought we would cover Devil Woman."

She almost choked. She had often helped her father breed a mare—or cover a mare, as it was more commonly called. And she knew that sooner or later she and Cade would have to do the same. But it took on an intimacy that she would rather forgo. However, she had little choice. Left to breed on their own, the horses sometimes hurt one another—something a horse farm could ill afford to let happen.

After she and Davey finished washing and drying the lunch dishes, she went out to the paddock. Her steps lagged, like a first grader's on the way to school. Cade was already showing the mare to the stud. The stud, a handsome bay stallion, thrust his head through the two-foot cutout in the pen's fence—just enough room to sniff the teasing mare and bite her neck in love play.

Cade held the feisty mare's halter as she bared her teeth and pinned her ears back. "Let's get on with it, Cass," he said.

All her life she had taken part in horse breeding. Yet now embarrassment tinged her cheeks. She took the mare's halter and held it while Cade hobbled the mare and wrapped her tail with a Velcro bandage to keep it out of the way during the time the stallion actually mounted her.

"You know," he said, and she heard the teasing in his voice, "mares are a lot like women. Some are shy, and shake and cower. Other mares pretend boredom. Then there are the wild ones. They fight the studs all the way, refusing to surrender until that very last moment."

The innuendo slipped by her. Her attention was piqued by some elusive thought that troubled her. "Where did you acquire such an intimate knowledge of mares?" she asked, her straight brows lowering with an uneasiness she couldn't put her finger on.

He paused, and when he replied it was with words that seemed to be carefully chosen. "Several years ago a big scandal broke out about the drugging of racehorses. I—uhh, went to work at one of the horse farms involved not long afterward."

She would have questioned him further about this revealing side of him, but the stallion emitted a deep whinny that was incredibly masculine in tone. She shivered at the sense of urgency that suddenly filled the air. The stallion's need to mate was something that was almost tangible, as real and urgent as the need that coursed between her and Cade.

Cade rose and said, "Okay, keep a tight rein on the mare, while I bring the stud around."

Cassie did as he told her, knowing that he was giving her the less dangerous job, since controlling the stallion, which weighed anywhere from one thousand two hundred to one thousand five hundred pounds, offered the most risk. Cade led the stud to the left side of the mare, rather than to her rear. Even with the hobbles, the mare could injure the stallion by kicking him. Cassie held tightly to the mare's halter while the stud sniffed and bit the mare's neck at the crest of her mane.

Coloring at the sensual foreplay going on before her, Cassie slid a glance at Cade. His sulfurous gaze riveted her where she stood. She saw in his eyes the same desire that knotted her stomach. She looked away. In her ears the frenzied neighing of the mare was drowned out by her own heavy breathing.

Suddenly the stallion reared up over the mare's back, his legs braced on her shoulders. His heavy weight pinned her motionless as he worked his way around to her rear. The mare tried to snap her head about in protest, but Cassie held fast. Devil Woman's eyes rolled in fury. She kicked viciously until the final moment, and then quivered in acquiescence. The erotic scene that took place was elemental and natural and, for Cassie, sensuously provocative as it had never been in earlier years.

What had happened to her? She was no longer the reluctant widow who had returned from New York. She wanted Cade, wanted him to make love to her with the same savage ardor that had possessed the stallion and the mare. Did that make her a wanton woman?

What disturbed her even more was the real-

ization that she was falling in love with Cade.
Her heart couldn't stand the pain of another
loss.

Cade's fingers rubbed the bridge of his nose.
He was tired. Leading a double life was getting him nowhere twice as fast. The words he
had written blurred on the tablet before him.
But he knew them well enough, knew that he
was incorporating Cass into his novel. He
hadn't planned on using her when he had
submitted the outline for his fact-based novel
about migrant workers to his publishers.

But her strong personality kept invading his
creative domain. There was a vibrancy about
her that radiated life. How many nights,
when he had come in late, had he stopped by
her bedroom door just to check if she was
sleeping? He couldn't count the number of
times he had paused in his work to watch her
cross the yard or jog down the road. He knew
intimately her small mannerisms, her habit
of playing with the indentation in her lower
lip when she was trying to think, or reaching
for an apple when she was nervous or irritated. The way she mothered Davey, lovingly but
not overprotectively, her genuine concern for
people—these were the things that endeared
her to him, memories he would treasure long
after he had left Lordsburg behind him.

He could hear the spray of the shower from
the bathroom, and his treacherous thoughts
shifted to mental images of Cass—her long

hair, wet, streaming down over her bare shoulders; rivulets of water sluicing down between rounded breasts . . .

He massaged his eyes, as if by doing so he could rid himself of his thoughts of her, rub out the images of her that crowded his brain when he should be thinking of the strike he was organizing or the book he had contracted to write.

Yet even as he resumed his writing a peripheral area of his mind dwelled on the Widow Woman. From that very first meeting he had known that he had seen her somewhere before. Cass's beauty wasn't the kind one forgot or mistook for someone else. Her looks were unique: a shade of hair that couldn't be skillfully duplicated with bleach, gray eyes that hid mysterious depths— reminding him of silent trees gray-bearded with moss—a too-wide mouth that he found totally enchanting.

When she had spoken to him of her past—of traveling through Europe with her husband— he had known he had his clue. A call to the Paris bureau chief for a prominent American magazine had given him the information he needed. It had been almost seven years before, when he was in Paris doing some investigative reporting for a New York newspaper. His job had been to root out the undercover operations of a Palestinian terrorist group operating out of France.

He had attended a party at the villa of a

well-known assembly member and become
quite bored with the social chitchat. Thinking
of leaving, he had changed his mind when he
saw the breathtaking young woman standing
in the double doorway next to the premier.
White hair was coiled in an elegant knot at
her nape, and a beaded white lamé gown set
off the golden glow of her healthy skin and the
smoky hue of her sensuous eyes. Every man
in the room had his covert gaze on the
woman, as did quite a few jealous wives.

With the intention of seeking her out, Cade
had set his champagne glass on the tray being
carried around by a purple-liveried waiter.
But an equally-bored attaché's wife with
henna-dyed hair had delayed him with flirtatious questions, so that by the time he reached
the doorway, the young woman was gone.

A few questions had revealed that she was a
haute-couture model of international fame—
and very much married. Her husband, he was
told, was a world-renowned Italian composer
with whose name he was only vaguely familiar, since music wasn't one of his more developed interests. After that he had put the young
woman out of his mind . . . or so he had
thought.

He heard the opening and closing of the
shower door. With a muttered curse he tossed
his pencil on the desk and rose to pace the
room. The closed bathroom door couldn't keep
him from her if he wanted to take her. But his
growing love for her was as good as a hundred

locks. He swerved back to the desk and picked up the pencil. He had been wrong to think that he could write an impartial novel about a subject that was so much a part of himself.

What he needed was a glass of scotch that was as old as he was.

Chapter 9

ANABERTA'S BLACK-AND-WHITE WEDDING PIC-
tures and a portrait of the Virgin looked com-
placently down on both the good-natured
woman and Cassie, who were on their knees
before the tow-headed four-year-old. The two
women were struggling to get the socks on
Davey's dirt-blackened little feet.

"It tickles!" Davey giggled, delighting in
the attention he was receiving from both
women.

"Just like his mama," Anaberta puffed. "Always running barefooted."

Cassie laughed and jammed a tennis shoe
over the wriggling foot, saying, "Sorry to be so
late in picking him up, Anaberta, but a call
came in just as I was about to leave the office.
Miss Creighburg again—complaining about a

teenager this time. The poor kid fell off his bicycle into her precious shrubbery and damaged the branches."

"You work too hard, Cassie. You know that Eric—he has the hot eye for you. Why don't you marry him? No more hard work and long hours. You'd have the easy life."

Cassie busied herself with tying the shoelace. "I like my job. Besides, you don't marry for the easy life, Anaberta. For me, at least, it'd have to be love."

Anaberta sat back on her plump haunches. Her gold teeth gleamed in the dimness of the small but immaculately clean house. "It's that ex-convict, isn't it? Montoya. One damn sexy man, I think."

"That's the trouble with everyone in Lordsburg," Cassie mumbled. "They're thinking too much."

"Sure we are." Anaberta looped a bow in the shoelace. "Us women think about what it would be like to have a man like Montoya bed us, and—"

"Anaberta!" Cassie admonished with a warning glance at Davey.

The woman cackled and winked lasciviously. "And the men, they think of nothing else but the Widow Woman. Each of those *hombres* wants to be the one to take away your grief."

"I'm not grieving!"

"Sure, you ain't. 'Cause you got a man like Montoya 'round your house, eh?"

Cassie rolled her eyes. "I give up. You only have one thing on your mind, Anaberta Aguilar."

"Same thing you do, Cassie Duval!" The woman cackled again.

Of course, Anaberta was right. But that didn't mean she was going to brazenly display her interest, Cassie told herself as she nosed the sheriff's car into the grove of cottonwoods by the garage and let Davey out to play. There was no reason why she couldn't try to think of Cade as she would any boarder she might have kept. As long as he did his work about the ranch she would continue to feed and house him. Otherwise, she was determined that she would give him no further thought.

So why was she looking around the yard for him and, when she didn't see him, listening for the sound of him moving about his room as she entered the kitchen? And why the disappointment, when he wasn't there, when she knew that he rarely returned until late in the evening, if that soon?

She hung her hat on the peg and, after removing the bullets from her .357, hung the gun belt next to the Stetson. At Davey's scream she spun for the door and ran outside. When she didn't see him, her heart thumped in terror. What if he had waded into the pond Cade had built? The water barely reached Davey's knees, but still . . .

She rounded the barn to collide with Davey. He fell back onto his little rear, but didn't relinquish the large white duck that filled his arms. "Look, Mama. Our duck!"

But she was looking at the man behind her son. He stood feet apart, arms crossed, smiling that lopsided grin of his that dug the pit in his chin deeper. "Armadeo's cousin scrounged up the duck for me," Cade explained.

"What shall we call him?" Davey asked.

"It's a her," Cade said. "I thought your mother needed another female around the ranch."

"How about Donald?" Davey said, unperturbed.

Cassie dragged her gaze away from Cade's face. "You don't name female ducks Donald."

The duck flapped its wings as Davey struggled to his feet. "Why not?"

She looked to Cade. "Why not?"

He spread his hands out, palms upward. His muscle-ridged shoulders shrugged, and she knew that he was trying to contain his laughter. "Beats me, Cass."

She sighed. "Donald it is, then."

Later, as she opened canned salmon for dinner, Cade volunteered to help her. "All right," she said, slightly amazed that he didn't think his masculinity would be threatened by working in the kitchen. But she said nothing further. Better to keep any conversation on an impersonal subject.

He filled the kitchen, obliterating everything in it, subduing the bright yellow and white, dominating her. While she busied herself dicing the celery into a ceramic bowl, he crumbled the crackers to mix with the salmon. She noted the way his massive hands pulverized them, disposing of the chore in seconds—more thoroughly than a rolling pin, more quickly than a blender.

"You're home early," she commented. That seemed a safe subject.

"I was on the phone all afternoon with state and federal agencies. I was so bushed, I took off early."

"Do you think the agencies really help?"

He brushed the crackers from his hands before answering. "Most of the time—no. They demand firsthand evidence and affidavits of wrongdoings. And usually they side unfairly with the growers, because it's businessmen who control the lobbyists who in turn influence the congressmen."

He was standing too close. Did her rapid breathing sound as loud to him as it did in her own ears? She crossed to the refrigerator to take out three eggs. "Why do the migrants put up with such treatment? Why don't they refuse to work for unfair growers?"

He took the eggs from her and cracked one over the bowl's rim. "Since a lot of the migrants can't read or write, they don't realize that they're being cheated on payroll taxes and other false deductions from their checks."

She watched him crack the second egg with

a hard rap that betrayed his anger. "What's pathetic, Cass, is that a lot of the migrants are Mexican-Americans—and they're still innocent enough to be blindly patriotic about the country that has used them so badly."

"That's not entirely true," she protested. "I've lived here long enough to see that the worst offenders are often those of their own blood—labor contractors, overseers, bosses— Mexicans whose families came to the United States a generation or more earlier. It's those very labor contractors who sell their own people in job lots to the growers, Cade; they're the worst evil in a system that's very close to slavery."

He grinned at her. "You should have been a lawyer instead of a sheriff or a model."

Her eyes narrowed. "How did you know that I had been a model?"

"Weren't you?"

"How did you know?" she persisted.

Without missing a beat, his gaze raked over her as he said, "You have the figure for it."

"So do a lot of women."

He shrugged. "I do a lot of reading. I could have noticed your photo in some magazine."

The explanation seemed inadequate, but perhaps she was too touchy about her former life. It was a part of her that she wanted to leave behind.

That night after dinner he did the dishes while she bathed Davey and tucked him into bed. When she returned to the kitchen Cade was putting the last of the dried dishes into the cabinet. A damp dish towel was slung over his shoulder. She stood uncertainly in the doorway. Through the screen door she could hear the clicking of the cicadas. With the rest of the house darkened and silent, the sound seemed to increase the intimacy between the two of them.

She should go on to bed, but it seemed rude to leave him without at least thanking him for his help. She walked over to the counter and reached for an apple in the fruit bowl, saying in what she hoped was a casual manner, "Thank you for doing the dishes, Cade."

She would have escaped to her room with the apple, but his whispered "Cass" halted her.

She looked back at him, trying to control the nervous thrill his low voice stirred in her. "Yes?"

He tugged the dish towel off his shoulder and crossed to her. She stifled the cowardly urge to step back at his approach. But then, there was nowhere to go; the refrigerator blocked her way. The hard line of his lips curved into a smile that had the power to devastate. She knew that he sensed her nervousness, but all he said was, "Give me your apple."

She passed him the fruit, an expression of curiosity furrowing her brows. "You should always wash your fruits and vegetables before you eat them," he said. "Picking crops taught me that much. The insecticide on them is sometimes enough to kill a rabbit."

She watched as he wiped the fruit gently with the towel, careful not to bruise the flesh. Experience had taught her that his hands could be just as gentle on her own flesh. Flushing, she raised her gaze to his. "Nowadays," he continued, "growers leach out a fruit's natural hue—and with it any nutrients. Then they shoot it full of artificial color."

He smiled and bit into the polished apple with his slightly uneven white teeth before handing the fruit back to her. There was something erotic about sharing the apple with him, and she knew he was fully aware of it. What he was doing was an act calculated to arouse her. It was a reversal of the fall from Eden, with Adam tempting Eve. Still, Cassie bit into the fruit, almost enjoying the hot light she saw flare in Cade's eyes when her tongue licked the apple's juice from her lips.

He braced a hand just above her head on the refrigerator door, and something in the quirk of his lips told her that he was picking up her challenge. She was certain of it when she saw the way his eyes grazed over her cleavage, which was exposed just above the low V of her shirt.

"You know, Cass, some growers pump a plant hormone into their fruit to make it fat and hard—the way some women pump silicone into their breasts to enhance them."

Her lips parted in a gasped O. He placed a

finger on her bottom lip. His smile was tender. "Don't play with me, Cass. I'm not the country bumpkin you might think I am. I can match all your tricks and more."

She caught his finger and pressed the half-eaten apple into his hand. "I'm learning that, Cade Montoya. I don't like it," she said honestly. "Because—I don't know why; I just don't. But I do know the games are over between us. It was dangerous of me to let our business relationship get out of hand."

His lids narrowed over molten gold eyes. "I hope to hell you have better control than I do," he said, and swung away, leaving her alone in the kitchen.

It started out with a trifling argument. The months of enforced intimacy had taken their toll on both Cade and Cassie. She got up that last Saturday in June feeling really good about the world. She had paid off the last of the vet bills, old man Haskell had recommended that her name be put on the election ballot as a write-in candidate—thereby lending her his indirect support—and the clinic had released Davey from the need for any further asthma shots.

Still in her caftan at eight in the morning, she stood out on the veranda and stretched, feeling the sunlight warming her flesh. Leaning against the rough cedar post, she languorously tilted her face to let the sun play on her closed lids. The lavender plant that hedged the veranda wafted its sweet fragrance upward to envelop her. She decided that she must have spring fever in the summer. She was happy with the world and her place in it.

At the droning hum of a car's engine she slitted her lids, resenting its intrusion into her quiet retreat. A whirl of dust traced the car's progress down the caliche road toward the ranchhouse. She straightened. Cade's station wagon. She had heard him leave earlier as she had been groping for her toothbrush. She had thought he was heading for the fields. They were to be thinned and hoed in preparation for a second fertilization the following week.

"Where've you been?" she asked in a voice drowsy with the morning's heat.

He strode toward the steps, and she saw the folded newspaper and envelopes he carried. He had gotten the mail for her.

His smile faded. "Do you always parade around outside half-naked so that passing strangers can fill their eyes?" he asked sourly.

"You're the only stranger who's been crude enough to 'fill his eyes,' as you so sweetly put it."

"If you wouldn't flaunt it . . ."

They met head on at the top of the steps. Her hands clenched. "You've invaded my house—now you're even invading the privacy of my mail! Next thing I know you'll be invading my bedroom!"

She snatched at the envelopes, but he

caught her wrist. "That's what you really want, isn't it? For me to invade your bedroom and take you by force, so you won't suffer the guilt of having given yourself."

"What?" she screeched, and jerked her wrist away so that the envelopes and the newspaper scattered like wind-whipped leaves over the steps and veranda. "Let me tell you something, Mr. Montoya," she said, her eyes flashing as she jabbed her forefinger at his shirt buttons with each clipped word she spoke. "Your ego is highly inflated. You're nothing but a common laborer who just happens to have an education and doesn't know what to do with it. You're the last man I would want to give myself to!"

His grin was mean and mocking. At that moment he looked ugly. "You know what, Widow Woman? I don't buy that."

"Ohhhh! You—you're incredible!" She stooped to grab up the mail that littered the steps. Tears of self-disgust blurred her eyes, disgust at the overpowering urge to surrender to him and to her own weakness. "You're detestable," she mumbled. "Abominable . . ."

He dropped to his haunches and caught her shoulders in a painful grip. "But not detestable enough for you to send me away. Not abominable enough for you to refuse my kisses."

His mouth took hers in an angry kiss. She shoved against the unyielding wall of his chest, her eyes glittering with her angry tears.

"Don't touch me! Your kisses are repugnant, do you hear me!"

His hazel eyes blackened like smoke pouring out of hell. He had the urgent need to find out what she was like when she let herself go. He shifted her weight, forcing her back against the stairs, and jerked the caftan's zipper down. As he buried his head in the exposed hollow of her shoulder, his lips claimed the soft flesh in a kiss of passion that he knew would leave a bruised mark by the next day. His hand pushed aside the robe to greedily cup her tender breast. He rolled it beneath his palm, and the feel of the soft tissue hardening beneath the heat of his kneading fingers set off the same hardening response in him.

It was broad daylight—someone could drive up, Davey could walk through the side door—but nothing at that moment could have kept him from her . . . until he heard her soft, surrendering moan.

He felt her fingers slip up to tangle in the wayward curls at his nape. And he hated himself then, hated what he was doing. He loved her. . . . He didn't want to hurt her . . . ever. He caught that slender hand and pulled it down to hold it between his two large ones. Looking down into her lovely face, he saw the confusion and hurt mirrored in those fantastic eyes.

"Cass . . . Cass, I don't know what's coming over me. I didn't mean for this to happen

. . . didn't plan it." He ran his long fingers through his hair. "Outside forces seem to be conspiring to pit us against each other, while our bodies—they defy all logic and practicality and good sense. All I can say is I'm sorry. Truly sorry, Cass. It won't happen again."

Her gaze had been lowered, unable to meet the impassioned honesty that illuminated his face, and the words from the open newspaper leaped out at her: REINHART DEFENDANT RULED INNOCENT. She picked up the newspaper and scanned the article.

On or about June 28 at the Reinhart Farms fields, located along Highway 338, County of Hidalgo, State of New Mexico, at or about the hour of 10 A.M. of the same day, defendant Roberto Manuel Rico, acting within the course and scope of his employment, did injure plantiff Librado Robles by hitting plantiff's body with a flatbed truck. The district attorney has ruled that no crime was committed and as such no warrant was issued.

A look of understanding lit her face. "This— this article . . . it's the reason for your foul humor this morning, isn't it?"

He nodded, his generous lips stretched thin. "It didn't help. Nor did the sight of your luscious silhouette, framed by the sunlight when I drove up, help to restore my equanimity. All the control I've been putting on myself seemed to just snap at that moment."

Her soft smile deepened the dimples in her cheeks, and he felt himself sinking ten fathoms deep. "I can empathize. We'll just have to be more guarded."

And that, Cade told himself, had probably been the last thing Caesar had thought before he went to the forum on the Ides of March.

Chapter 10

"Jonathan Reinhart, President of Reinhart Farms, has announced the second quarter's profit earnings at slightly less than a two percent increase over the same quarter of the previous year. 'We had expected more, but then, we have to accept that times are tough—especially for farms like ours.'"

Cade's laugh was bitter. He folded the copy of the *Lordsburg Independent* from which he had been reading and tossed it into the Charger's back seat. "Farms? Industrial plantations would be a more accurate description. I still find it incredible that Rico got away with running down Robles.

Cassie flashed him an exasperated look. "I

talked with the witnesses, Cade. Both workers and pickets admitted that Robles had been cursing and spitting at Rico. The fact was that Robles openly provoked Rico into losing his temper."

"Assault and battery was not a viable solution to the problem, Cass."

She returned her attention to negotiating the lanes of traffic on the busy interstate. When Cade had asked for a ride up to Santa Fe with her, explaining that he had lent his car to Armadeo again, she had entertained reservations about the feasibility of spending such a long period of time alone with him. The trip was a minimum seven-hour drive each way—fourteen hours total in which to forget all the warnings and lectures she had given herself about the danger of falling in love with a wandering man.

After that explosive confrontation on the porch several days earlier she would have evaded the issue by taking a plane—except that the nearest commercial airport was in Silver City, and the flight required a transfer to another commuter line before she would land in Santa Fe.

As it was, when Cade asked for the lift he had raised his fingers in the Boy Scout sign and said, "Scout's honor, Cass. I promise not to force my wicked attentions on you again."

His grin had been devilish, revealing his strong white teeth, and she had snapped, "I doubt you were ever a Boy Scout, Cade

Montoya. I have an uncanny suspicion that you're a wolf in Scout's clothing."

At least the three-day training session at the Law Enforcement Academy would keep her too occupied to see him or think about him.

"You mentioned talking with the Migrant Ministry in Santa Fe," she said, not taking her eyes off the highway. "Couldn't you have called just as easily?"

Cade slumped comfortably in the seat, his hands behind his head, one booted ankle crossed over his knee. "I—uhh, had some research I wanted to do for HCFWA at the capitol building library. Microfilm, archives, things like that."

Her dark brows lowered in a puzzled frown. "Like what? How would that help HCFWA?"

"Now you sound like a sheriff—asking investigative questions." His lips crooked in an appealing grin. "I much prefer you as the Widow Woman."

The conversation was growing too personal. As it was, she found it impossible to think of Cade in the terms used by Eric—activist, agitator, an undesirable element. For her Cade was very desirable. Never had she been caught up in the throes of such sensuality as she was with this one man. She had experienced romance with Mario before their marriage. But romance one entered into willingly, actively. Sensual enthrallment—one had no choice.

She shifted in the seat, tired after the hours

of driving, and her skirt slid up past her knees. As she tugged the hem down she caught Cade's wicked glance of amusement— and something else before his lids dropped to hide his gaze, a look of raw desire. Its intensity was stunning. An alarm went off inside her.

"When will your work be finished in Lordsburg, Cade?" Better to remind herself how unwise it would be to fall in love with him.

For a moment he didn't answer. Then he said, "I never set a goal. The laborers need a cooperative food store, a workers' clinic, a dining hall and kitchen. Armadeo has already started a union newspaper. And Ramona is working on a credit union." He smiled. "Her syntax is abysmal, but she has a way with figures."

For sure, Cassie thought jealously, and wanted to kick herself for inadvertently resorting to Cade's colloquialism. "Why do you do it, Cade?"

His face settled into a hardness that she didn't often glimpse. "Signs in stores and restaurants that I remember from my childhood. *White Trade Only.* And *No dogs or Mexes.*"

Her idea of migrants had always been one of light-hearted gasoline gypsies. Cade was making her see another side, a side she didn't want to see. Not just because it was unpleasant, but also because it made her see the qualities in Cade that she admired and respected. His leadership, his concern for people, the gentle mystic in him that illogically combined with the ruthlessness of the tough labor leader. He was an enigma—a man who people willingly followed, who men wanted to emulate and women wanted to love.

Dangerous, the direction her thoughts were taking. Yes, definitely dangerous.

The highway that followed the green path of the meandering Rio Grande and bisected Albuquerque with a conglomeration of modern overpasses, loops, and cloverleafs demanded Cassie's attention, which was difficult, since she was all too aware of the vigorous man next to her . . . of his strong black brows and the hazel eyes that didn't seem to go with his dark hair, and yet did. There was something stormy and magnetic about him that she couldn't quite identify.

North of the large city the landscape once more turned to brown rolling hills barren of all but low-growing cacti. The mauve Sangre de Cristo mountains, named the Blood of Christ for their purple reddish hue, towered in the background. Their foothills reached out like giant arms to cradle the old world town of Santa Fe.

Cassie loved Santa Fe. It was older than either Jamestown or Plymouth Rock, and enchanted visitors with its winding cobblestone streets, where glistening white stucco houses with red-tiled roofs rubbed elbows with art galleries and fine shops.

La Villa Real de la Santa Fe de San Francisco—the Royal City of the Holy Faith of Saint Francis—allowed no neon lights in the city proper, nor any structures over two stories. All buildings had to be of either Spanish territorial or pueblo architecture. Neither railroad trains nor commercial jet-liners disturbed the city's peaceful setting. It was a romantic place—one she should never have agreed to be alone in with Cade Montoya.

In the tree-shaded plaza she halted before the La Fonda Inn, which marked the end of the Old Santa Fe Trail. Only the Palace of the Governors was older—the oldest public building still in continuous use in the United States —and it showed its age. The La Fonda, on the other hand, had been renovated many times since its construction in 1610 and was considered one of the most fashionable of hotels in which to stay. It was a place out of keeping with the unpolished image of the man next to her.

"The course finishes the third of July," she said when he got out and came around to her side of the car. "I'll pick you up here that afternoon, all right?"

He surprised her by cupping her neck and drawing her head through the window. His mouth claimed hers in a gentle kiss that was both warm and searching. Forgetting all her good intentions, she parted her lips, her tongue answering the quest of his. Her hand crept up to cradle his jaw, her fingers delighting in the roughened texture of hit-and-miss shaven skin.

Horns beeping from behind reminded them that she was stalling traffic. Cade drew away and winked. "Take good care of yourself, Cass."

In bemusement she watched him stride off into La Fonda's lobby; then she put the car in gear, gratifying the impatient drivers behind her, and drove out to Cerrillos Road and the Law Enforcement Academy.

The law enforcement course was to be a short, intensified one that would demand the students' full concentration. But over the next three days Cassie barely heard the lectures, delivered by uniformed policemen and casually dressed professors. Instead her mind too often drifted to thoughts of Cade, visions of his well-honed body, memories of his glances, his touch.

Fortunately she was already familiar with a lot of the subjects covered by the academy: radio dispatching; homicide investigation; search and rescue; and jail management, which included the areas of feeding, doing laundry and caring for the inmates. A field trip was made to the crime lab, where she learned to lift fingerprints and set plaster casts for footprints. Every afternoon was spent on the firing range in target practice, where she scored 288 out of a possible 300.

At night, in the sparsely furnished dormitory room that had been provided, she studied everything from the minute details of investigating the scene of a crime—securing the area from contamination of the evidence and carrying out a systematic search—to such superfluous facts as the derivation of the word 'sheriff'—from the English *shire*, or county, which had had a headman known as a "reeve," thus the title of "shire reeve."

The three days of lectures seemed interminable. On Friday afternoon she collected her certificate and drove back into Santa Fe proper. The streets were already jammed with Fourth of July merrymakers, and in the plaza the Indians had their turquoise jewelry and leather goods displayed on spread blankets of every intense color. Here and there booths were being erected for the next day's pancake breakfast and the festivities that would follow.

She found a parking space on San Francisco Street and walked the short distance to La Fonda Inn. The desk clerk at the historic hotel gave her Cade's room number. The room was on the second floor, and as she waited for the elevator to reach its destination she had a funny feeling in the pit of her stomach that had nothing to do with the rising of the elevator. The memory of Cade's parting kiss three days earlier was making it very difficult for her to treat their relationship platonically. Friendly—that was just how she would have to keep their conversations on the return trip. Friendly and polite. That way she would have no broken heart after he left Lordsburg.

At her resolute knock, she heard drawers shutting. Then Cade opened the door, a note pad in his free hand. His shirt was unbuttoned and the shirt-tail was hanging out. For a moment he stood there, his eyes moving over her, taking in the soft rose crepe blouse and toast-colored A-line challis skirt that showed off the shapely curve of her long legs. She had removed its matching jacket against the summer heat and carried it over one arm.

"You left your hair down."

The simple statement was her undoing. If he had said that he wanted to take her to bed, she could have coolly handled the pass. But the one comment—in a voice rife with tightly bridled passion—sapped all the strength from her legs so that merely standing required all her effort.

She searched for some adequate reply, but was saved the necessity of making one when he took her hand, drawing her into the room. It was richly furnished with plush chocolate brown carpet and a salmon-pink velvet spread and drapes that were splotched with shades of rust brown—hardly consistent with Cade's nonexistent income. No doubt some church charity or human rights organization picked up the tab.

"You look tired, Cass," he said, tossing the

pad and the pencil lodged behind his ear on the rich mahogany desk. "Hard day?"

She nodded, relieved that he had opted for that conclusion. "A hard three days."

His bronzed chest drew her gaze, and she was barely aware that he led her to the king-size bed, a waterbed that gently buoyed her weight, and sat her down. She was startled when he dropped to one knee and removed the open-toed slings from each of her feet.

"What are you doing?" she stuttered.

He grinned. "Rubbing your arch. Therapists claim it helps alleviate tired muscles."

The muscles in her calf tensed. "I don't think it works."

His hand slid up the line of her calf. "You have to relax, Cass."

His fingers massaged her tight muscles. Involuntarily her lids drooped at the pleasurable sensation. She reclined back on her elbows, arching her foot as a contented cat would its back. Her head lolled backward, spilling her hair across the spread. A languorous feeling seeped through every nerve cell in her body, rendering her totally relaxed. "Hmmm, Cade," she murmured indolently, "what you're doing . . . it feels heavenly."

His hand centered in the hollow of her knee. She had had no idea the spot could be so erotically sensitive. Her breathing was shallow, her pulse erratic. His hand paused in its stroking. Her eyes flew open. He was watching her. She flushed, embarrassed at being caught at a revealing moment. Inhibited, she jerked her foot away. "We better be going. It's a long drive back."

"For sure," he said softly.

He came to his feet, blotting out everything else in the room, and calmly rolled down his shirt sleeves and buttoned his cuffs. His dark face wore a detached look, as if he hadn't been at all affected by the sensuality of the moment. She slid to the edge of the bed and rose, inordinately absorbed in smoothing her skirt's wrinkleless fabric. His very nearness made breathing difficult, rational thinking impossible. Common sense whispered that she should get out of the room as soon as possible.

When his fingers went to the zipper of his jeans, she turned her head, busying herself with the vitally important task of collecting her clutch purse, which was still lying on the bed where she had left it. "I'm only tucking in my shirt, Cass." His voice was low and gently mocking.

"I'll put on some lipstick while you finish." She escaped to the bathroom, a gleaming chrome and tile affair. Her hand shook as she applied the apricot tint to her lips. Her skin was colorless, her dark brows and lashes the only shading. Even her deep gray eyes had paled to the color of an eerie morning mist. Then the large mirror was suddenly filled by Cade's reflection behind hers. A secret look appeared in her hungry eyes.

He reached around her and took the lipstick tube from her unresisting fingers. "Cass," he said huskily, turning her around to face him. "I missed you." His forefinger traced the bow line of her upper lip. "I need you. I need your loving. I need your soft touch."

Her eyes were large and pleading. She braced her hands against his chest. "Cade," she whispered, "no . . . please . . . not me."

"I don't want anyone else, Cass. Only you. I can't help myself. The way you look at me . . . I'd have to be lobotomized not to know what you're feeling." His hand cupped the underside of her breast, and her eyes closed against the torch his touch ignited inside her. "I feel it, too," he rasped. "The wanting. These three days have been hell. It's tearing me apart. Being so near you—and not being able to hold you . . . to touch you . . . to kiss you. . . ."

Her forehead dropped against his chest. "I can't give myself so easily." Her voice was muffled by his shirt, and he tilted her chin upward, his eyes searing her face with his passion. "What you want from me, Cade . . . For me, it could only mean total surrender."

His lips brushed hers, even as his fingers found her nipple through the thin material of her blouse. "I don't want your surrender. . . . I want your participation."

The protective wall that she had carefully erected over the years and that dammed up her controlled emotions broke. The painful

need of another human being, stifled all that
time, flooded over her, releasing her at last.
She gave to him the participation he asked,
returning his kiss with a fervor that surprised
her until she forgot that surprise—and all
else.

With the ease of a man accustomed to ex-
acting physical labor, he lifted her onto the
tiled counter. Above them the bathroom's
bright white lights shone with an intensity
that was as stimulating as a colored strobe
light.

"Cade . . . don't let me think beyond this
moment."

"We're two people alone in the world," he
said, his mouth burnishing its way down her
arched neck. "Let me love you, Cass."

She couldn't have denied him, even if she
had wanted to. His lips covered hers and
breathed tobacco-scented air into her mouth,
air that flowed down into her lungs and was
distributed throughout her blood system, so
that he was as much a part of her as if he had
entered her.

Her own hands loosened her blouse buttons
and the flimsy bra's front clasp to free her
breasts for his sustenance. She held his head
to her and watched, her excitement growing
so that she made no protest when his hands
levered her upward so he could slide her
pantyhose and lacy briefs down over her
thighs.

What happened was an act of raw passion

that met the desperate needs of two lonely people. Her hands gripped his powerful shoulders, and her legs wrapped about his buttocks. Each time his torso slammed against hers, her hips arched toward his. She followed his lead, returning his thrust with her own driving need. Her vulnerable womanhood welcomed his throbbing strength, and what could have been a weapon of torture became an instrument of love.

A multitude of incoherent thoughts tumbled through her mind like dried sagebrush in a spring sandstorm. She feared that he would stop, that it would not be enough. She wondered why she had waited so long to experience this primitive side of passion. And then all thought was banished by the spiraling, incredibly intense pleasure that left her weeping in astonishment.

The red tip of Cade's cigarette glowed in the predawn darkness. Absently Cassie rubbed her cheek against the hair that curled crisply on his chest. She remembered waking up often in the deep of night after Mario had died, desperate with the need to be held—not a sexual need, just a very human need to be touched, comforted, embraced. Cade's muscular arm about her shoulders answered that necessity, reassured her. Yet . . .

"What is it, Cass?" he asked in that deep, rumbling voice of his. His fingers, toughened by manual labor, stroked her bare arm just above the edge of the rumpled sheet. "What is it that's bothering you?"

His perception dismayed her. Mario, whose songs had had the power to move people to the depths of their emotions, had too often failed to perceive the emotional needs of the people in his personal life. Either he had never realized, or he had ignored the realization, how much attention she and Davey had craved from him. She never knew which.

Cade reached over to grind out the cigarette in the ashtray on the nightstand and turned so that he was propped on his elbow, looking down at her. His fingers lifted her chin; his eyes, shadowed with concern, searched her face. "The truth, Cass . . . nothing less between us."

Her lids lowered, her long, thick lashes lying like ebony fans above her model's high, upswept cheekbones. "Shame," she whispered. "Shame that I could be lying in a hotel bed with a strange man. . . . I'm old-fashioned, I guess, despite the jet-setting image I acquired in New York." Her eyes slanted up to meet his probing ones. "And desperation, Cade. Because I know I can't let this happen again."

A half smile etched his deeply carved lips. "Adam and Eve were strangers—and I don't think a preacher blessed their union."

Her head moved in a small, negative gesture. "It's not necessarily marriage I'm talking about, Cade. But a commitment. I've been

brought up to believe a commitment is vital
between two people or else . . . or else what
happens . . . is—is mere copulation . . . like
the stallion and the mare."

He rolled over onto his back, his arm across
his forehead. After a moment he said, in a
voice void of emotion, "My commitment is
elsewhere, Cass."

The pang of his words was too much. Holding the sheet over her breasts, she sat up,
stretching to reach her slip, which was draped
where Cade had carelessly tossed it at the foot
of the bed.

As her hand clutched the satiny fabric,
Cade said, "Cass, stay." His fingers traced the
graceful line of her spine down to its
erogenous base, and she shivered with the
sensual sensation that eddied through her.

As if he perceived the sexual arousal his
touch communicated, he quickly withdrew
his hand. "Stay for the weekend, Cass. I
want—I need—your company. I promise nothing else will happen."

"I—I can't. Davey is—"

"Call Anaberta. Ask her to keep him for you
just through Sunday."

Cassie looked over her shoulder at him. She
had no idea what a provocative picture she
presented, with her hair draped like a silken
curtain over her shoulder and her model's
perfect white teeth playing with her bottom
lip in indecision. Could it be so wrong? she
asked herself—one weekend of shared enjoy-

ment? It would hurt no one . . . not if she went into it with her eyes wide open to the knowledge that Cade was the roving kind, that there could be no permanence to their relationship. It could be a pleasant memory to treasure long after he had wandered on.

She smiled, a shy, cautious smile that wrapped around his heart. "All right, Cade. What's on the agenda?"

He grinned lewdly. "First, let's get dressed. I don't think I like the idea of other men looking at your sexy naked body."

With an impish smile she flung her slip at him. He caught the silky, flimsy undergarment and, laughing, roped it around her shoulders, drawing her over to him. The sheet fell away to reveal her firm breasts, the brown halos tantalizingly dark against the milk white flesh. The laughter faded from both their voices. They looked into each other's eyes, seeing there the poignant longing.

Cade thrust the slip at her. "Get dressed," he rasped.

Chapter 11

RISING BEYOND SANTA FE'S ANCIENT AND HIS-
toric plaza was a magnificent view of the
Sangre de Cristo peaks. That morning the
plaza's booths were already packed with
Fourth of July's merrymakers—cowpokes in
from surrounding ranches; tourists lugging
cameras; Indians dressed in brilliant-colored
velveteens; and unfashionably dressed scien-
tists down from the Los Alamos atomic research center.

Mariachi music mingled with the intermit-
tent whoomp of fireworks. The pungent smell
of the tamales from a nearby vendor's grill
mixed with the sweeter odor of the Mexican
candy hawked by the old *dulce* woman. And
all about, the air was pervaded with the scent
of eucalyptus and orange blossoms.

Cade found a shade-dappled spot beneath an elm where the two of them could feast on their stacks of pancakes, cascading with melted butter and maple syrup. Sitting on the cushiony grass, Cassie tucked her legs beneath the flounced skirt of her white peasant dress. She had knotted a scarlet sweater about her waist for use later against the evening's cool mountain air. As usual, Cade was dressed casually in tan cords and a brown plaid shirt. The long sleeves had been rolled up over his forearms so he could more easily attack the sticky breakfast.

She leaned toward him and rubbed her forefinger along the corner of his lips, wiping away a smudge of maple syrup. "Don't," he warned, "or you'll make me forget all my good intentions, and I'll make love to you right here on the grass."

"Does syrup ever get into the indentation in your chin?" she teased.

"Has anyone ever told you that you're an impudent young woman?"

She smiled archly. "Now I know why Spanish is called a romance language. All you Hispanics are romantics at heart." She nodded toward two dark-eyed maidens, whose raven black heads were covered by white lace mantillas. They flashed flirtatious glances at two men with large sombreros and boldly flowing mustaches who passed in the opposite direction along the promenade.

Cade never took his burning gaze off her.

"My Hispanic blood makes it very difficult for me to ignore romance's wild callings."

"Well, try. Because it won't do either of us any good, Cade Montoya."

The reply was made in jest, but both knew the unstated seriousness that underscored it, and so they attempted to treat the rest of the day's outing in the same light-hearted vein.

Hand in hand they wandered through picturesque art galleries and historic buildings with smoke-blackened ceilings. They ate a lunch of *carne adovoda*, beans and *pozole* on the private patio of a thick-walled century-old convent. "I'm glad you never made the decision to become a nun," Cade said in a bantering voice. "What a waste it would have been."

"You would never have made a monk," she retorted. "The nuns' virtue would have been perilously jeopardized."

But over their cups of tangy *cafe de olla*—Mexican spiced coffee—their eyes spoke of all the other things that their lips could not say.

That afternoon they watched the parade with the multitude of other revelers. High school bands led by majorettes with pasted-on smiles, Indian dancers beating drums and tortoiseshells, and Mexican *caballeros* mounted on prancing palominos passed before the spectators. Cassie leaned her head against Cade's shoulder, and he put his arm about her waist. It was as if they couldn't touch each other enough.

And always there was the specter of their

restrained passion—a still unfulfilled passion
—that followed their footsteps and haunted
every glance they exchanged and word they
uttered. They seemed to actually radiate a
fervor so intense that people turned their
heads to stare with envy when they passed.

After the last band member had marched by
Cade looked down at her. "You have your
choice of entertainment for this evening—the
opera, the Festival Theater, or the fireworks
display."

Fireworks were already going off inside her
at his nearness. She lowered her lashes to
hide the need of him that surely showed in her
eyes. "The opera."

Strauss's *Salome* was playing in the open
air opera house. Above the audience, stars
twinkled in the black velvet night sky. Spo-
radically their sparkle was paled by the brilliant burst of fireworks. The air turned chilly
with the night, and Cade draped Cassie's
sweater about her shoulders. When his large
hand dropped to rest possessively on her
thigh, her sharply indrawn breath was
drowned out by the tenor voice of the German
singer soaring into his aria.

Their late dinner was eaten by candlelight
in La Fonda's intimate dining room, decorated in the traditional New Mexican style with
rustic, massive wood furniture. The home-
made sangria could have tasted like epsom
salts, and Cassie would not have noticed.

She was in love with Cade, and the realization made her illogically both miserable and ecstatic. She wanted to cry; she wanted to laugh. She wanted to run her fingers through his thick, unruly hair, to feel the strength of his arms about her waist, molding her against him, to experience again the depths of his passion.

How could this one man—a rough-hewn, common laborer—be so attuned to her soul, so sensitive to her emotional needs? Why did he have to be the one she had fallen in love with—some anonymous transient who followed the seasons? What would happen to her and Davey when he roamed on to another town?

And later that night, after dinner—what then? How could she deny him—or herself— the love she desperately wanted to experience with him again?

She lifted her eyes from the crimson liquid in her glass to meet Cade's discerning gaze. "How did you make out with the Migrant Ministry?" she asked, hoping to distract his nimble mind from uncovering her trail of thoughts.

He shrugged, and she guessed that he knew exactly what she was thinking but was going along with her charade. "All right. Since migrant workers are often wetbacks, they don't apply for any help from social services because of their fear of *La Migra*. But at least I've talked the Migrant Ministry into helping in setting up a meeting with the owners of the chain stores to support a boycott of Reinhart chiles—which will not endear me to Jonathan Reinhart."

She knew that Cade might be hated as well as adored, but she was certain that he couldn't be judged on the same terms as a man with ordinary talents and ambitions.

His hazel eyes took on an animated glow, giving them that peculiar golden cast. "You know, Cass, when the grape workers struck several years ago, the longshoremen refused to load the growers' grapes at the docks until the farm workers were given more humane treatment, better working conditions. That's what I want to see happen in Hidalgo County before—"

"Before you move on," she finished quietly.

The rest of the dinner was eaten in a strained silence. After Cade paid he said, "I think we better drive back tonight."

She knew he was right. "Of course."

While he collected his things in his hotel room, she waited just inside the doorway, her palms braced against the open door to support her trembling body. How could her wild wanting of this stranger weaken her so? She watched with a painful yearning as he stuffed several books, some papers and his shaving kit into a canvas bag before he turned to face her. His face was set in a craggy mold, his eyes bleak, his lips hard. But his words were taut with caring.

"I'd like to keep you here, Cass. I would

spend the night making love to you . . . kissing you, holding you, loving you in marvelous and mystical ways I never bothered to with any other woman."

"But you don't love me enough to stay," she stated in a quiet voice.

He dropped the bag and crossed the room to her in two strides. Taking her in his arms, he drew her head into the hollow of his shoulder. "To give what I feel for you a name is to cheapen it, Cassie. But you must know that it's so powerful that, if it were misused, it could cause irreparable harm, unbearable pain. I wouldn't do that to you."

Her words were muffled by his shirt. "Cade, I can't go on this way, living in the same house with—"

He tilted her head back and kissed away the tears that spiked her lashes. "Don't send me away, honey. Being around you is like standing in the sunlight. Let me stay with you and Davey at the ranch until it's time for me to go."

She nodded, wishing she could still the rapid pounding of her heart. Her parted lips felt the butterfly brush of his before he set her from him. "We better start back. Davey will be anxious for us to return."

"Now, Cassie," Eric said in his most persuasive tone, "you know I've been wild for you since high school." He laid his arm across the Steakhouse's oilcloth-covered table and clasped her hand. His Nordic eyes burned as blue as the flame of the table's candle. "I want to marry you."

"I've been married, Eric. Once is enough."

And there could never again be a man to fill her heart, her soul, her entire body as Cade did. But she could not have Cade. Was that why she had accepted Eric's dinner invitation? Had she truly hoped that Eric would make her forget Cade? Foolish of her. More than a month had passed since her return from Santa Fe, and all she could think about was him. A part of her wanted to send him away, to ease the sensual tension that pervaded the house; another part of her knew she would shrivel up like a tumbleweed if he left . . . *when* he left.

"Your son needs a father, Cassie. I'd try to be a good father to him."

That was a new tactic. She wryly wondered if he even knew her son's name. She thought about Jonathan Reinhart, trying to picture him as a grandfather. Cold and calculating. Davey would be miserable living under the old man's thumb. And so would she.

"I'm offering you an agricultural empire, Cassie. No longer would you have to demean yourself doing a man's job."

She withdrew her hand from Eric's. "I like my job. And it's not necessarily a man's job."

Eric's lips curled in a supercilious smile. "Don't tell me New York turned you into a militant feminist."

She reached for her shoulder bag. "My lunch hour is almost up."

He reached across and caught the strap of her shoulder bag, halting her. "You're making a mistake—siding with that agitator."

Annoyed, she gritted her teeth at the possessive way that his hand, hazed with light reddish hairs, clutched her bag. Her gaze swept up to his square, ruddy face. For the first time she noticed how much the son resembled the father. When thwarted, Eric's mouth curled in that same mean way Jonathan Reinhart's did. "I'll tell you the same thing that I told Cade."

He squinted, his eyes becoming small pale-blue stones. "Cade, is it?" he sneered.

"I'm not siding with anyone. I am enforcing, and will continue to enforce, the law—impartially, fairly."

His voice softened its biting tone, his words almost coaxing. "Think about what I've said, Cassie, before you turn down my offer outright."

She jerked the bag's strap from his grasp and rushed out of the booth. She couldn't get out of the Steakhouse quickly enough. Her skin was chilled as she hurried out into the hot and windy August afternoon, almost colliding with Marilyn.

"Cassie!" The redhead laughed and shifted her sack of groceries in her arms. "Where you going so fast—to answer a burglary call?"

"Sorry, Marilyn." Cassie resettled the bananas that threatened to fall out of the bag. "I wasn't looking where I was going."

Marilyn sighed. "How could anyone see where they're going the way the dust is swirling? Curly claims if we don't get some rain soon, all of Lordsburg is going to blow away. And I flatly refuse to dust the furniture one more time this week."

Cassie managed a smile for her friend. "I quit dusting months ago."

But when she would have left, Marilyn forestalled her, saying, "Cassie—a magazine I bought last week, I've been meaning to show it to you. This writer—he won some kind of award from the—oh, some university or something on that order—"

"Yes?" She really needed to get back and relieve Hernandez. "What about the writer?"

"Well, Cass, he had the same first name as that convict of yours, the one who's working for you."

"He's not *my* convict. And he's a *former* convict, anyway, Marilyn."

The young woman smiled knowingly. "You're defending him like you might care a lot about him, Cassie."

"What about the writer?"

"Oh, well, he's named Cade, too—Cade McDonald, no—Cade McPherson. That's it. Cade McPherson."

"And? . . ."

"You must admit, Cade is an unusual name. And, Cassie, the photograph—well, it was an old one. One of those black and whites. But it did resemble the stranger working at your ranch."

Cassie smiled. "Exactly—a stranger. How many times have you actually seen Cade Montoya? Three or four? I bet you couldn't pick him out in a police lineup."

Marilyn grinned triumphantly. "I got you there, Sheriff. Your convict—uhh, your hired hand—isn't a man a woman is likely to forget."

"I wish I could," Cassie mumbled and, bidding a hasty goodbye, left her friend.

Chapter 12

WITH LABOR DAY AND THE BEGINNING OF THE chile-picking season came Cade's hope for a strike. The young woman with the baby on her back—Cassie never found out her name—was the first to walk off the fields and give her name to the labor agent whom Cade had arranged to be present.

Two days later Lordsburg received the first influx of television crews and newspapers as the U.S. Department of Labor declared the strike certified.

Along with the smattering of reporters, Cassie patrolled the Reinhart fields that had been scheduled to be picked. The tension that leaped like a current between the striking pickers and Reinhart's people, facing each other across the dirt service road that fronted the dark green fields, was almost palpable. It was as though the dust-blotted sky warned of turbulent days to come.

The conveyor belts that were to load the hand-harvested chiles into gondolas were silent and motionless in the empty fields. The harvesting of chiles, like tomatoes and other easily bruised vegetables and fruits, could not yet be profitably automated.

A woman reporter, who looked more like a wrestler, flagged down Cassie's four-wheeler on the service road. Cassie pulled over into the pampas grass, and the woman leaned in the window to ask leading questions that would titillate her newspaper's subscribers.

"Do you think it's true that the AFL-CIO encourages racial discrimination?"

"I wouldn't know."

The woman scratched out something on her note pad. "But the town of Lordsburg—would you say that it's involved in racial discrimination?"

Cassie was losing her patience. "That's something you'd have to ask the *campesinos* —the farm workers."

"What about the strike leader—this Montoya? Jonathan Reinhart called him a disruptive factor in today's society. Have you ever had any dealings with him in your capacity as sheriff?"

The questions were getting too personal. "He has no record with the Lordsburg County Court System," she replied tersely and pulled the vehicle back onto the road before the reporter could rap out any more questions.

Let Cade fend off the news media. It was his fault that trouble was exploding in Lordsburg. It was his fault that she was in love with him.

The strike appeared to be a standoff until two days after the news media, bored with the inactivity, pulled out of Lordsburg. Then Cade called. "A gasoline-soaked rag wrapped around a rock has been thrown into our offices," he said.

It was the first time that she had heard his deep, rumbling voice since—almost since Santa Fe, it seemed to her. The two of them had gone out of their way to avoid being along with each other—she leaving early in the morning for the office, he not returning to the ranch until very late. Like two feuding parents, they passed any necessary messages by way of Davey.

But they weren't feuding. It would be better if they were, Cassie thought ruefully after she hung up the receiver. She dreaded going to the HCFWA headquarters to fill out the complaint report. It would mean talking with Cade face to face, all the while trying to keep the betraying need of him out of her voice, out of her eyes.

The old grocery store's glass window had been shattered. She parked the car in front of the headquarters. Inside, Ramona, sweeping up the shards of glass, flashed her a disgruntled look. When Cassie walked into Cade's

office his broad back was to her as he pointed
out sectors on the wall map to a short brown-
skinned man. The sight of Cade's powerful
body set her off all over again. How could she
maintain an impersonal, professional conversation when she wanted him so badly that she
hurt, as if a garrote were constricting her
heart and lungs?

Standing in the doorway, she had made no
noise; yet Cade, warned of her presence by
that highly refined sixth sense he seemed to
possess, turned his head to fix her with a
penetrating gaze. She noticed that he was
hollow-eyed from lack of sleep. He nodded a
dismissal to the man at his side, who doffed
his hat in deference as he passed her.

When they were alone she said, "You look
grim. This was what you wanted, wasn't it?
The farm workers' confrontation with Reinhart."

He splayed his hands on top of the desk. "I
missed you, Cass."

She stiffened, and he said, "Sorry, forget I
said that. Yes, the confrontation is necessary.
But violence isn't. I was hoping to avoid it.
The HCFWA still can—if I can keep hotheads
like Librado Robles from retaliating."

"Has he done anything?"

"Not yet. That's why I wanted to file a
complaint. To keep the process lawful. If the
farm workers can see justice being carried
out, they'll abide by the law."

She sighed and, taking a seat beside the

desk, pulled out her pen and notebook. "All right. Do you know who was responsible?"

"Take off your hat, Cass." He moved to stand before her. "Let me see your hair."

"Don't," she whispered. "Don't make it harder for us than it already is."

He ran his hands through his rumpled hair and turned from her. "Armadeo was working late when the rock was thrown through the window. He ran outside in time to see Rico driving off in the farm truck."

"I'll question Armadeo and Rico, but I doubt if the Magistrate's Court will find sufficient evidence to try Rico."

Cade frowned, looking ugly and fierce. "So do I, Cass. But if they don't . . ."

He didn't finish the sentence. Both of them knew that violence would erupt, focusing the attention of people throughout the United States on Lordsburg. Cassie's hope of a quiet life for her and Davey seemed to be as false as rapidly as the weather forecasters' predictions of rain for the area.

She rose to go. "I'll file the Offense Report and keep you informed of its progress."

As she reached the door he said, "Cass."

Slowly she turned. "Yes?"

"How's Davey? I've been too busy to get a chance to see him."

She knew that that wasn't all he had been about to say. "He misses you, Cade." *And so do I.*

* * *

At last the rains came. Torrents poured down from the sky to deluge the desert. The lightning scissored across the heavens, illuminating every mountain crevice, and the wind howled out of the canyons, bowing the paloverde and cottonwoods under its force. The rains would harm the chile crop and delay the harvest, but, then again, few chile fields were being harvested.

Cassie lay in her bed, wide awake. She turned her face to the digital clock. Two-forty. Had Cade come in yet? She didn't know; the wail of the wind could have drowned out any noise of his arrival.

Since the strike had begun a week ago, his bed had not been slept in. Directing the many phases of the strike was consuming all of his time; yet she noted that the chores about the ranch were taken care of—the stalls cleaned, the horses groomed. He had to be returning to the ranch during the day, snatching a few hours here and there to take care of whatever needed to be done about the place.

Between the crackling and popping of the lightning, the thunderous banging of the barn doors could be heard as they were slammed against the sides of the barn by the wind. Cassie squinched her eyes closed. Her body rebelled against leaving the comfortable bed to brave the storm. But the knowledge of how costly it would be to replace the stored hay if it were ruined by water brought her guiltily upright in bed.

With a sigh she slipped into her furry mules and, zipping the comfortable blue flannel caftan up over her, paused to look in on Davey. He was folded nearly double, his mouth open in deep sleep. Reassured, she tiptoed past to the kitchen. At the back door she grabbed the umbrella before she went out into the rain-swept night.

It was like the heavens had turned on a gigantic faucet. The umbrella proved useless; the wind had sprung its ribs before she made it halfway across the yard. By the time she reached the barn her robe and gown were soaked. She struggled with one door, pushing it closed with her weight. The other door swung wildly. She flung herself against it, but when she would have shoved it closed, the small heel of her mule clogged in the mud, tripping her. She sprawled face first.

At once crying and cursing, she pushed herself into a sitting position. Her hair was plastered to her face and neck by both the rain and her tears of frustration. She thought that nothing could be worse—until headlights swept the yard, and she recognized the car. Cade's old station wagon.

Any hope that he might have missed seeing her was extinguished when his massive frame sprang from the car and he sprinted toward her. His large hands slid beneath her armpits to hoist her upright. "Cass," he muttered, holding her against him. "Are you all right?"

She nodded her head. It was all she could do. Her entire body trembled, and she knew that without the rocklike support of Cade's solid body she would collapse.

"The storm got me to worrying about you—I came as soon as I could."

The rain poured about them, molding their clothing to their bodies, molding them to each other. Her arms clung to his shoulders. "Cade . . ."

It was the slightest whisper, made almost inaudible by the banshee howling of the wind. Still Cade heard it. In the darkness his mouth found her upturned face, searched feverishly for her parted lips. The kiss was as violent as the storm. His mouth ground down on hers. Her teeth bit his lower lip. His tongue lashed her mouth's soft recesses.

"*Querida, mi alma, mi corazon,*" he rasped when at last his mouth released hers.

His whispered words of love were enough; she gave herself up to the strength in the hands that pressed her down to the rain-pummeled earth. The waiting seemed unbearable for her as he discarded his clothes. With the wind and rain thrashing the two of them, he was but a shadow above her.

Then he crouched over her like the lone wolf he was, unashamed of his boldly displayed virility. His eyes glowed golden in the rain-whipped darkness. His wet hair clung in riotous curls to his forehead and his neck. She watched as he unzipped her robe and spread it open. When the two ties on her gown did not give, he ripped them. The rain pelted her bare skin, until he stretched himself over her. She welcomed his warmth, gloried in his heavy weight.

He took her with a fierceness as elemental as the wrath nature had unleashed about them. The white-hot fire that blazed between them would not be quenched as they came together in a frenzy, their arms and legs interlocked in intimate juxtaposition. Her body arched to meet his, accepting the ferocity of his thrust. Her fingers dug into the muscles that corded his back. His hips slammed into hers. Her low passionate cries mingled with his husky murmuring of her name, over and over like some Latin liturgy. Their bodies were slippery with the mud and the rain and the hot sweat that poured from them in their ecstasy.

"Oh, God, Cass," he groaned, levering himself from her. "What have I done?"

She pushed back the swath of drenched hair from his eyes. "No, I wanted you to. I wanted you, Cade."

He rolled to his knees and gathered her up easily against his chest to carry her into the shelter of the barn. Her arms, encircling his neck, reluctantly relinquished their hold as he laid her on a bed of straw. Its fresh scent filled the barn, wrapping the two of them with its sweet incense. His hand brushed at the mud that smeared her cheek before he deserted her.

She called out his name in a cry as mournful as the wind, revealing her despair and longing. The only answer was the squeaking of hinges as the barn door was closed. Outside nature thundered out its rage upon the land. She struggled to sit upright, the straw tickling her flesh. Her eyes strained in the darkness to find him. Would he leave her now that their resolve to avoid the fulfillment of their passion had been shattered?

Then he came silently through the darkness to her, lowering himself over her to enfold her in his arms. Her relief was so great that she had to stifle her spontaneous words of love. Surprise followed as she was enfolded in a warm, scratchy blanket. It smelled of leather and horses, its earthy odor managing to excite that primitive part of her womanhood.

But Cade held her close against him, warming her, as he spoke in a quiet, firm voice. "We've gone too far to turn back, Cass. We'll talk later. But now . . . now I want to love you as you should have been loved . . . to love you as I've thought about and dreamed about doing a thousand times all these tormented months."

Kisses as light as meringue puffs were dropped on her lids, his hot breath fluttering her lashes. He pushed back the damp hair that was plastered against her cheek, so that the pale strands were meshed with the straw just below. His tongue flicked intoxicating paths along the delicate rim of one ear. "Cass . . . *mi amor* . . . without you there is no night or day for me."

His fingers pushed aside the blanket, and he pressed his face between her breasts, his hands teasing the faintly-veined globes with sensuous strokes.

"Cade, I love you . . . love you. . . ."

Her words trailed away as his head turned, his mouth seeking her passion-wrinkled areola. His jaws tugged in a sweet sucking motion that brought an enraptured sigh from her lips. When his teeth gently captured the hard brown nipple, she gasped at the exciting combination of pain and pleasure that spun its magical web throughout her.

His hands seductively explored the curves and indentations of her body, setting her afire with the tender yet roughened touch of his fingers. "Open yourself to me," he instructed in that bewitching, growling voice of his. Bemused by the play of his hands, the enticement of his voice, she complied like one entranced.

His fingers moved lower to the protective folds that were moist with her intensifying need of him. She clutched his shoulders as an incredible sensation spiraled through her. "That's it," he coaxed, his fingers gradually increasing their tempo. "Wait for it. It's coming."

Her back arched as her body was convulsed with a pleasure that defied description. Afterward she lay quiescent in his arms, a languorous inertia settling its net of lassitude over her. "I've wanted to do that for you for so long," he told her, his breath fanning the hair at her temples.

Her forehead nuzzled against his beard-stubbled jaw. "So that's the way of love," she murmured in a voice filled with marveling.

Her fingers slid downward and gently closed about him. She delighted in the feel of him. When she applied a delectable pressure she was rewarded with his soft groan. "I'd be derelict in my duty if I didn't reciprocate the pleasure, Cade Montoya."

Chapter 13

"CADE McPHERSON. SEE," MARILYN POINTED, "that's his name. But the photo does look like Cade Montoya, doesn't it? When I was house-cleaning I ran across the magazine again and decided to take another look at the article. What do you think?"

Sunday's sunlight was blinding, and Cassie moved beneath the shade of the church's twisted, mammoth cottonwood to focus more clearly on the photo. She tried to ignore Davey's tugging at her raspberry chiffon dress. Sitting still in church had drained him of all patience, and he was ready to go home and play. She was ready to return home, also—to Cade.

The night before she had half cajoled, half insisted that Cade get some sleep. She had tucked him into his bed as she would a protesting Davey, brushing the luxuriant hair back from his temples as she watched his lids resist closing, then finally surrender to his body's utter weariness.

That morning she had refrained from waking him, letting him get his much-needed sleep. Whatever had to be said between them could wait. They had waited this long to admit their love; the rest of the words could come later. She was in love. It was enough.

Shutting out the droning conversations of the people who still lingered in the churchyard, she tried to concentrate on the one-column article below the hard-to-distinguish photo.

Cade McPherson recently honored by the American Academy for Arts and Letters

In a career that has spanned a dozen years as a newspaper reporter, a staff writer for an international magazine and the author of five books, he has won several awards for investigative reporting. He is noted for his in-depth portrayals and exhaustive and prodigious personal research. His skillful handling of unusual subject matter, which satisfies the reading public's endless fascination with bizarre behavior, makes him a superior writer of realistic nonfiction.

He is reported to have once commented, "I write exclusively in the nonfiction
area, though my style is novelistic. Yet I
always stay within the framework of real
life, for I feel that it's more vivid and
challenging than anything I could dream
up as a novelist, at least at this stage of
my career."

Wordlessly Cassie handed the magazine
back to Marilyn. A sick feeling sloshed in the
pit of her stomach. "Well?" Marilyn asked. "Is
it him?"

Not trusting herself to speak, Cassie shook
her head in a gesture of uncertainty. Blindly
she groped for Davey's hand and pulled him
along with her to the four-wheeler. Were the
two men one and the same? Could Cade have
betrayed her trust? The questions rang
through her mind, tolling like a funeral bell a
thousand times on the drive back to the
ranch. As she pulled into the pebbled drive-
way she saw Cade out at the paddock, running a brush over Devil Woman. He waved
and started toward her with that graceful,
rolling stride of his, but she didn't wait.

After sliding from behind the wheel, she
hurried into the house. Behind her she heard
Davey call out merrily to Cade. The door to
Cade's bedroom stood partially open. She
pushed past it and crossed to her father's old
desk, pulling the top drawer open. Pencils,
pens, paper clips. She yanked the top right-

hand drawer . . . and froze. The drawer was crammed with loose lined papers—all filled with heavily scrawled words. She could close the drawer; she didn't have to read what was written. She could pretend that . . .

With icy fingers she picked up several sheets, rifling through them. Words leaped out at her—chile farms, growers, industrial plantations, migrants, sheriff. Her eyes halted at that word and returned to reread the paragraph.

A young woman of uncommon blonde beauty, Cate was both the sheriff and the Widow Woman to the people of the small farming community. And every male—

"So you know."

Cassie whirled, her back to the desk. Cade stood framed by the doorway. Behind him was Davey, a puzzled frown shadowing his little face at the tension he sensed between his mother and his friend. "How could you do it?" she snapped. "Even the name—Cate—you couldn't have chosen one any closer to my own."

His face was expressionless. "You took over my thoughts, Cass."

The papers she held fluttered like autumn leaves to the floor. " 'Bizarre behavior'!" she spat, quoting in scathing tones from his biography. " 'Vivid and challenging'! Is that all we were to you?"

"You know that's—"

"You used us," she charged in a tone drained of emotion. "You exploited us."

He started toward her. "I never meant for it to happen like it did." He caught her shoulders, his hazel eyes dark with intensity. "I never meant to fall in love with you."

She shoved him away from her. "Love? That's just another word for your books!"

He made no move to touch her again as she closed her eyes, her teeth biting her lip to stop its trembling. When her lids opened, tears glistened in her eyes. "I thought I loved you, Cade."

"Cass, listen to me—"

"Oh, how you pretended to sacrifice for your glorious cause!" she said caustically. "Why, you almost had all of Lordsburg believing you were some saint come to deliver the farm workers from their tribulations. Masquerading as a pauper, castigating the growers for their greed, when you probably make twice as much as they do and more. The noble, altruistic Cade Montoya—no, Cade McPherson, isn't it? You lived here with us under false pretenses—and a false name, even!"

He planted his hands on the desk to either side of her. "I'm both McPherson and Montoya. Montoya was my mother's name."

She pushed at his arms, but, like a drilling rig's thick, steel cable, they did not give. "Let me go," she whispered rawly. She was dangerously close to crying, and she didn't want to. She didn't want to show her weakness before this man who had used her so badly.

"No. Not until you hear what I have to say." Over his shoulder he said, "Davey, go outside until your mother and I finish talking. We'll get that ice cream soda I promised you later."

Davey looked worriedly from his mother back to Cade. Then, jamming his hands into his pockets, head down, he scuffed his tennis shoes as he made his way down the hall to the kitchen.

After Cade heard the side door slam he grabbed her upper arms and jerked her over to the bed. Thrusting her down against the mattress, he half sprawled over her, his heavy leg skimming her skirt in a tangled bunch above one thigh. His fingers grasped her chin and forced her to look at him. "Now you're going to listen to me, Cass."

"I don't want to hear anything you have to say. I just want you to leave—now!"

"Not until you've heard me out. I go to great lengths to research my books as accurately—"

"That's quite obvious."

His fingers dug into her shoulders. "If you don't shut up for just a moment, I swear I'm going to shake some sense into you. Now listen, Cass—I never deceived you. I did grow up as a crop picker. I did live as a migrant worker. That's why it was so important for me to do this book, my first novel. I knew first hand the atrocities perpetrated against the farm workers. Nor did I deceive you about my plans—I warned you I would be moving on."

Her eyes flashed. "Oh, you didn't lie to me about anything. You just didn't tell me about everything. Sin of omission and all that."

"I couldn't tell anyone, at first. The migrants are clannish, suspicious people. They wouldn't have trusted me if they thought I wasn't one of them."

"So you deceived them. How noble of you."

"Damn it, I don't feel noble. I've been feeling rotten ever since I started falling in love with you. I wanted to tell you, but I knew this would happen. I knew once I did, I would have to leave."

"And lose your marvelous opportunity to write the bestseller of the century all about our scandalous community. How unfortunate for you."

"Hell!" he muttered impatiently. "You're not ready to listen." His mouth ground down on hers, tasting the tears that salted her lips. "Cass . . . Cass," he mumbled, "don't fight me. I want your love, not your anger."

She jerked her head to the side, escaping the domination of his lips. "Anger? That's not a strong enough word. My God, I despise you, Cade McPherson!"

He levered himself upright, his hands still pinioning her arms to the rumpled sheets. His lips were flattened in a harsh, ugly line. His eyes gleamed above his hard cheekbones, dark and thunderous. "You're so righteous about the truth, aren't you? But you sure as hell aren't ready to face the truth when it's about yourself."

She glared up at him. "I don't know what you're talking about."

"I'll tell you. As an adored and motherless only child you led your father around by the nose—"

"That's not so!"

"And then Mario—"

"How dare you!"

"How dare I tell the truth? Remember, I'm an excellent investigative reporter. Your New York acquaintances and business associates were quite willing to reveal that Mario was deeply infatuated with you, with your beauty—"

"You went snooping into my past?" she gasped. "Asking personal questions about my marriage?"

"—that as your career soared, Mario doubted his own abilities and turned more and more to alcohol . . . that your desire for your own success drove him to kill himself with drinking and a fast, sordid life."

She covered her face with her hands. Her shoulders shook. "I tried to stop him," she cried. "I tried so much that I think he hated me toward the end."

Cade caught her hands and forced them

away from her face. "No, he loved you as helplessly as everyone does, including me, Cass."

"Words!" she cried. "Don't forget I know now how good you are with words. What do you do—find a woman to sleep with, to make love to, for every book you research?"

He flushed, and she laughed bitterly. "Too close to the truth, aren't I? Oh, you love me, don't you, Cade? But not enough to stay. Now, get out! Get out!"

"I won't let you lead me around by the nose as you did your father and Mario, Cass. Is that what you want—for me to leave?"

"You have the gall to ask me that—when you've been planning on leaving all along? Well, I'm finished furnishing your sexual recreation, Mr. McPherson. Go research a brothel next time."

"I didn't realize it was my sexual needs you were interested in all the while," he said in a dangerously soft voice. "But then, you know what one hears about widow women, Cass— those seamy stories about their sexual fantasies and pent-up frustrations."

Her hand arched upward to leave a red imprint on his jaw. "You—you're despicable!" She was oblivious to the black glitter in his eyes. "You're a low, vile—"

His hand caught her wrist in a manacled grip, snapping her up against him. "But not too low or vile to go to bed with, am I?" His fingers entangled themselves in her long, thick hair and tugged until her face was tilted up to his. He brushed his lips in a tantalizing gesture against her cheek, murmuring, "Perhaps we should try to re-create the magic between us one more time before I—"

"Get out!" she screamed, and shoved him away with a strength generated by her rage and hurt.

Standing, he gave a low laugh. "You should have known better than to bed down with a wandering man, Cass."

She stormed past him as he hunkered down to gather up the manuscript that she had scattered across the floor. Outside Davey sat on the steps, his stubborn little jaw sunk between his fists. He looked up when she shut the screen door behind her. "Are you finished fighting with Cade, Mama?"

She crossed to the veranda post and leaned against its rough cedar bark. Not wanting her son to see the tears that stung her eyes, she gazed out toward the far pastures, where the quarter horses grazed with indolently switching tails. "Yes, pet. We're finished arguing. . . . We're finished."

He shot to his feet. "Good! Now Cade and me can go into town." She looked quizzically at her son, and he hastened to explain, "He promised me a soda."

With the back of her hand she wiped surreptitiously at her eyes. "I don't think he'll be able to do that now, Davey. You see, he's going away."

Davey frowned, as if he found it difficult to follow his mother's train of thought. "He wouldn't go away, Mama. He's gonna buy me a—"

The screen door swung open. Cade stood there, his canvas bag slung over the back of his shoulder. "Cade!" Davey said. "Tell my mama you're not going away."

Cade's face was set in granite lines. He looked from Davey to Cassie. She turned her back on him. "I have to go, son," he said softly.

"No!" Davey cried.

Cade swung past him and, taking the three stairs in one stride, crossed to the station wagon. Davey started after him, crying, "Don't go away, Cade. Come back!"

Cassie grabbed at her son's waist and tugged him back against her. "He's got to go," she said gently, praying that her voice wouldn't break as she wiped the tears from Davey's cheeks, still rosy with baby fat.

"Cade . . . don't go!" the little boy yelled.

"Of course, I was upset by Cade McPherson's deception," Cassie told Marilyn, and shoved closed the drawer to the departmental file cabinet. "And I'm damned angry at the way Cade has broken my son's heart." And her own. But her lacerated pride wouldn't let her admit it, even to her friend. "Davey worshipped Cade."

Marilyn smiled sympathetically. "I'm

afraid Reinhart Farms doesn't share Davey's hero-worship," she said as she rose from the chair next to Cassie's desk and crossed to the door. "Curly said that old man Reinhart is choleric about tires that have been slashed on Reinhart Farms trucks and the fields that were flooded when the irrigation gates were mysteriously opened during the night."

Cassie sighed. "I've already received a personal complaint from Eric against Cade."

Knowing Cade's commitment to nonviolence, she doubted that he was responsible for the acts. But she wasn't about to defend him. Her hurt and anger only made her want to retaliate . . . to strike back, though she knew it was a childish response. What was worse was her consuming jealousy. Hernandez, who seemed to have some kind of uncanny grapevine, had revealed that Cade was staying with Armadeo—and just happened to add that the strike leader had been seen the night before at the Hidalgo Hotel bar with Ramona.

Cassie fervently hoped that the strike would be settled and a contract agreed to soon so Cade would leave town—and her thoughts. That last night when they had made love—the night of the thunderstorm—had left its mark on her in the form of a bad cold that seemed to get progressively worse. For days she had carried a handkerchief before her nose, which was red from violent sneezing.

She stopped in at the drugstore for an antihistamine, and Curly recommended that she go immediately to bed, "or else you'll wear your body down until pneumonia puts you into the clinic."

She couldn't afford to let that happen, and she reluctantly did as he advised. But she only felt worse the next day. Her head spun, and the thermometer indicated that she was running a low grade fever. Marilyn came over, poured orange juice down Cassie's throat, fed her a handful of vitamin C tablets that Curly had sent with her and took a dejected Davey back to her house to spend a couple of nights.

By the next evening Cassie felt no worse, at least. But a general weakness pervaded her as she moped from the bed to the kitchen and back to the bed again. The aspirin she had taken didn't help her throbbing headache. When she didn't even feel like reading the historical novel on her nightstand, she knew that she was really ill. Whenever she closed her eyes she saw Cade emblazoned on the backs of her lids, so she lay on her back in the darkness, watching the moon make sinister streaks of light that dappled the ceiling, and feeling all around miserable.

Trustingly she had given her love into Cade's hands and had been betrayed. True, Cade had never come right out and told her that he loved her before that final confrontation; true, he had made it explicitly clear from the start that he would be leaving one day; and true, he had stolen nothing from her—she had given herself to him willingly, foolishly.

What hurt her so painfully was his deceit, his duplicity. He had used her, manipulated her for his own ends. She remembered the night when they watched the mare foal, how he had questioned her about her past, about her husband.

Her fists crumpled the chenille bedspread at the thought of his conniving, sly methods. Investigative reporter! He was a sneaking weasel! Oh, how he must have laughed! What amusement she must have provided him. And what a story line for his novel!

And Davey, poor Davey. Her own hurt turned into boiling anger for the way Cade had stolen the boy's trusting heart and then so easily abandoned it. Damn Cade Montoya to everlasting hell!

As if her thoughts had conjured him up, his voice thundered through the house. "Damn it, Cass, what kind of sherr—sheriff are you if you don't even keep your own doors locked?"

His voice was slurred, and she knew instantly that he was drunk. She sprang to a sitting position in the bed, pulling the covers up over her chest. She heard him trip over the magazine rack and the muttered curse that followed. Her heart beat erratically against her ribcage. Anger coalesced with fear to render her paralytic.

Like a wraith from another world, he materialized in the doorway. In the darkness she could barely make out his features—except for his lambent eyes that glowed opalescently.

"Get out!" she whispered, surprised that her lips had managed to obey her brain's frantic signals.

He weaved toward her, and she cried out, "If you don't leave immediately, I'll—"

"You'll what?" he demanded with a low laugh. "Call the sherr—sheriff?"

"Damn you, just leave me alone!" Her shaky voice told her that she was dangerously close to hysteria, and she tried to control it. "Haven't you done enough?"

He leaned over the bed and put his fists on the mattress at either side of her thighs. His face hovered scant inches from hers. "I won't leave 'til you tell me what I want to know."

She could smell the alcohol fumes on the warm breath that fanned her face with each word he ground out. "I've told you too much as it is, Cade Montoya. Now get out! Get out of my house and out of my life!"

His hands shot out to wrap about her upper arms, his grip bruising her flesh. "Hernandez told me you left the office sick yesterday. Are you pregnant, Cass? Are you carrying my child?"

Her mouth fell open, and she blinked her astonishment. "Am I carrying your child?" she echoed in a stupefied voice. Then she understood, and she began to laugh, laughter that slid into the hysteria she had feared.

He shook her, and her head snapped back and forth like a rag doll's. "Stop it, Cass!"

"It's so funny!" she gasped.

As if suddenly sobering, he released her. Tears coursed down her cheeks, and he brushed them away, saying in a voice full of self-loathing, "Oh, God, what a mess I've made of things, Cass."

His voice, which had deepened, had a calming effect on her. She wiped the back of her hand across her still-wet cheek, saying, "What irony! Davey and I couldn't hold you here, but the thought that I might be carrying your child brought you back on the double."

His hand captured her wrist. "Damn it, Cass, what kind of monster do you think I am? Do you honestly think I'd go off and leave you to bear our child alone?"

"Do you honestly think I'd welcome you into my house after what you've done?"

She tried to jerk her hand away, but he held fast and the two of them went sprawling on the bed. His heavy body pressing her into the mattress, he pinned her wrists to either side of her shoulders. "No matter how much you might hate me," he gritted, "I wouldn't go off and let you have our baby on your own."

"Don't tell me you were this concerned whether any of the other women you made love to got pregnant."

"No," he said in a voice that was pitched low with his wanting. "You're the only woman who has ever mattered to me, Cass."

"Mattered—but not loved."

"That's just it, Cass. I do love you."

At one time those words would have flooded

her heart with the deepest kind of joy.
Now . . .

"But not enough to stay," she said tonelessly. "Not unless your guilt compelled you. And
I don't want you that way, Cade." Her voice
hardened to hide the tears that choked her
throat. "Damn it, I don't want you—period!
Not any way! Not ever!"

"I don't believe you." His head lowered,
angled, so that his mouth could claim hers in
a punishing kiss.

She wanted to twist away, to escape the lips
that incited her passion. But her love for him
was greater than her pride, and she moaned
her shuddering despair against his mouth
before succumbing to the sensual onslaught
of his kiss. Her mouth moved beneath his, her
lips parting for his invasion. His tongue rav-
ished her mouth.

"Cass," he groaned against the hollow of
her neck, "it's been hell not finding you when
I wake in the morning. Not seeing your fresh
face or hearing your soft, warm voice."

"I was trying to learn to get along without
you," she whispered, staring blindly at the
dark ceiling. "Why did you have to come
back?"

"I'm tormented by—" He broke off, his body
stiffening. His hand slipped up to cup her
neck where her pulse beat. "My God, Cass,
you're burning with fever!"

I'm burning with my need for you. But the
interruption gave her the impetus to smother

the fire his kiss had built within her. She wriggled the upper half of her body from beneath his. "That's what I've been trying to tell you," she said in a precise and formal tone.

She felt his narrowed eyes watching her as she scooted away; then she leaned against the backboard, drawing her knees up close to her chest. She wrapped her arms about her knees to stop her trembling. Despite her fever, she was icy with the cold that seeped clear through to her bones.

He rolled to his side, propping himself up on one elbow. "What have you been trying to tell me?"

"That I'm not carrying your child. That night in the barn"—she was furious that her voice was unsteady—"I caught a cold. I'm sick—that's all. Not pregnant! So you don't have to worry about hanging around Lordsburg on my account!"

"I see."

She heard the inflection in his voice, but couldn't identify it as relief or disappointment. Her pride rebelled, and she snapped, "No, you don't see! You don't see anything but your own selfish needs."

He uncoiled his length and rolled to his feet. "And yours aren't selfish, Cass? You refuse to give love freely unless your demands are met —unless Mario sacrificed his career for yours, unless I capitulate and bind myself to this claustrophobic town."

"You bastard!"

She couldn't see his face, but she could hear the black fury in his voice. "You go to church, you read the Bible. What did Paul tell the Corinthians about love? Love isn't possessive. But that's all you know, Cass. Possessions— this ranch, the horses, your sheriff's badge. Do you call that loving, Cass? Spare me your acts of love, then!"

Her chin lifted imperiously. "Will you leave now?" She only hoped that she could maintain her facade of indifference until she heard the side door close.

Chapter 14

CASSIE'S COLD FINALLY RAN ITS COURSE. BUT
she was still sick at heart. She dreaded seeing
Cade, running into him somewhere on the
street. Fortunately, she didn't spot his station
wagon near any of the farms she patrolled.
The smaller farms had long before been
picked, their mature green pods loaded in
boxes that waited in packing sheds for transportation to market. At the farms that weren't
strike-bound, pickers were already laying the
riper red chiles out on raised metal roofs to be
sun-dried, or drying the crimson pods the
old-fashioned way on strings, called *ristras*.

The only thing Cassie thought that she
might dread as much as running into Cade
was the looming possibility of a confrontation

with old man Reinhart. And that came the following week, when Robles's wife entered the sheriff's office. A small, bony woman in a black mantilla, she stood with her back to the door, as if any moment she would bolt. Her black eyes were dark hollows. The pinched look on her face betrayed her nervousness. As though changing her mind, she turned to open the door.

Cassie quickly intervened, asking politely, "Can I help you?"

The woman wheeled like a cornered animal. "No . . . I . . . I come to the wrong place."

Cassie rose and crossed to the pathetically thin woman, taking her elbow and gently guiding her toward the chair. "What is it, Mrs. Robles?"

The woman's lips quivered; her hands fidgeted with the rosary she held. *"Mi esposo*—my husband—the Reinhart men come to our house. They take him away." She raised her terrified gaze to Cassie. "You must help him, *señora.*"

Cassie was amazed that this woman, whom everyone knew was often mistreated by her husband, would actually plead for help for him.

The amazement must have shown in Cassie's face, for the woman said, "Others—they do not understand my husband. He barks like a mean dog. But it is because of his shame.

Because his wife and children must work in the fields. Because the *jefes*—the bosses like Rico—they shame him before us. What he does to us . . . to others . . . *señora*, it is the only way he knows to . . ." She paused and waved her hand uncertainly, as if she were seeking a word to better express her thoughts. "It is the only way Librado knows to walk like a man."

The woman's poignant words touched Cassie to the core. In spite of what the man did, the woman loved him. And in spite of what Cade had done, Cassie knew that she, too, loved *him*. She could have told him that she was pregnant, bound him to her that way—if only for a little while. But it wouldn't have held him. He was a wandering man, a man who needed to be free.

Cassie ushered the woman to the door, saying, "I'll check on your husband, Mrs. Robles."

On the drive over to the Reinharts' city warehouse and packing sheds, she told herself that she was wasting her time, that Robles was probably drunk out of his mind somewhere, that . . . that . . . damn it, none of the problems would have arisen if Cade hadn't come to Lordsburg to stir up trouble. Her hands clenched the steering wheel at the thought of him.

Eric was standing on the loading dock when she wheeled into the parking area reserved for the diesel trucks. His eyes lit up when she got out of the car, and a large smile that seemed to her almost triumphant creased his lantern jaw as he loped down the steps to meet her. His gaze blatantly raked over her curves, which were enhanced by her white jeans, and dipped past the V-neck of her cotton shirt to flagrantly peruse the valley between her breasts.

She resented his crassness and tried to control her temper. "Hello, Eric."

"Cassie! I knew you had changed your mind about us Reinharts when I heard the word that Montoya was no longer working for you." He caught her hand in a grip that seemed to pulverize her fingers. "It's about time you fired that troublemaker."

She pulled her hand away from his. "That's not why I came, Eric."

His brows furrowed over the bridge of his nose. "What is it, then?"

"Robles. His wife came to my office today. She claims your men hauled him off."

To his credit, Eric was embarrassed. "He ran amok. We had to do something."

"You can't take the law into your own hands. Where is he, Eric?"

His eyes narrowed. He jammed his fists on his hips, his head jutting forward. "So that's the way it's going to be—you against us."

She didn't back down beneath his rage. "What have your men done with Robles?"

"We haven't hurt the swine, sweetheart.

Just teaching him a lesson about damaging Reinhart property."

Her lips stretched out in a thin line. "What kind of lesson?"

Eric shrugged. His grin was smug. "Rico dropped him out in the desert—near Hell's Furnace."

Cassie bit her bottom lip. Too often Mexican nationals fleeing Mexico during the summer months died when "coyotes," a Hispanic term for smugglers, abandoned them in Hell's Furnace, a vast stretch of boiling desert between the border and Lordsburg.

She swerved away from Eric and slid behind the wheel of the Charger. He caught the handle just as she reached to close the door. "Don't do it, Cassie. You go against us on this and your job as sheriff is finished. My father will see to it that the largest smear campaign ever launched destroys your election bid."

Her heart lurched, but she managed a shrug. "I think the citizens believe that I have performed responsibly as sheriff thus far."

"Really?" His smile was demonic. "Living with a man without the benefit of a marriage license? That doesn't sound like the kind of upright image Hidalgo County would want its sheriff to have. How long do you think it'll take once we Reinharts put out the word that you're unfit for the office before you're drummed out of Lordsburg? Why, even your horse ranch won't keep food on the table, because there won't be a soul in Hidalgo

County who would risk the Reinhart wrath by dealing with you. If my father has his way, you'll wind up eating horsemeat."

Without another word she jerked the car door closed. In the rearview mirror she could still see Eric, his legs spread in a menacing stance as he watched her drive away. Her hands trembled on the steering wheel. Was it worth it, jeopardizing her job for a farm worker for whom she had no respect? Robles was a worse troublemaker than Cade. The thought of Cade caused her stomach to burn with bitterness all over again. After the way he had deceived her, used her, hurt Davey—she would have to be imbecilic to feel any loyalty to him or his cause.

At the crossroads outside Reinhart Farms she halted the four-wheeler. To the north lay Lordsburg, and to the south, thirty-five miles down the road, lay Hell's Furnace. There was absolutely no reason in the world why she should buck the Reinharts for a worthless man like Robles. Intelligence and logic stood on the side of preserving her job.

Cursing her foolishness, she wheeled the vehicle south toward Hell's Furnace.

Twenty-five miles down the highway the pavement changed abruptly into a corduroyed dirt road. As the four-wheeler bounced down into *barancas* and crested rocky ravines, she began to wish that she had returned to the ranch first for one of the quarter horses. Most county sheriffs' vehicles in New Mexico were equipped with a hitch for pulling horse trailers. A horse could often negotiate the treacherously rugged landscape of desert, canyons and mountains that even a four-wheeler couldn't.

Heat waves shimmered above the desert floor, making it difficult for her to focus accurately on distant objects. Even jagged Animas Peak that marked the Continental Divide wavered like a mirage. Belatedly she checked her gas gauge. Less than a quarter of a tank. She flipped off the air conditioner and rolled down the window. The heat slammed against her like a sudden blast from a steel mill's coking oven.

With a dwindling gas reserve, she would have to find Robles soon. As a precaution she decided to radio Hernandez. He could notify the Border Patrol at El Paso to help in the search—and possibly her own rescue, if she should run out of gas.

Her mobile unit emitted only static. She pressed the mike's button again. "Hernandez, this is Mobile Unit 471. Do you read me?"

Crackling static.

She was too far out, beyond the transmitter's range. Despite the heat, a chill dotted her arms with goose bumps. Without water a human couldn't survive very long beneath the death-dealing sun that made the white desert sand asphalt-hot. Not even cacti could gain a foothold in the unyielding sand and rock where temperatures at ground level soared to one hundred and fifty degrees. Within a matter of hours dehydration could parch the tongue so dry that swallowing would be impossible.

Anxiously her eyes searched the desert floor. Robles could be nearby, but hidden from sight in some *baranca*. She could only hope that he would hear her engine. What if the mountains' coolness had enticed him to head in that direction? He would doubtless fail to realize that the foothills were further away than they appeared. He would never make it walking.

She could still turn the four-wheeler around. She judged that she had enough gas to at least make it back to the pavement, where she would be more easily found. Her mind wavered in indecision. But, unwisely, her foot pressed down on the gas pedal.

She forced herself to scan the hot, shimmering horizon. Fifteen minutes later she was rewarded. Her eyes squinted at the tiny distant figure. It did indeed move. "Robles!" she breathed aloud.

As the four-wheeler drew nearer, the man's arms waved frantically in the air. *"Señora!"* he croaked when she drew up beside him. His cheekbone was badly bruised. With his black hair powdered white with sand and his swarthy face scorched a ruddy shade, he looked more like a Scandinavian than an Hispanic.

He staggered, then fell against the hood,

and she jumped out of the car, running around to catch him. When she slid her arm under his shoulder to support him, she could actually feel the heat radiating off his skin, as if his body were an iron. She grunted beneath his weight as she hobbled with him toward the back door and shoved him prone on the seat.

"Librado Robles," she rasped more to herself than the semiconscious figure, "you owe me a tall glass of ice-cold lemonade." The thought of the cool refreshment made her mouth water. She swallowed back her thirst and climbed into the front seat. Forget the glass of lemonade. Soon—soon she could order an entire pitcher.

She kept a worried eye on the gas gauge as she drove. The black needle bounced ominously below the E mark. How much reserve did she have—two gallons? Some five minutes later the engine sputtered, and the Charger rolled a couple of yards. Then the engine coughed, the vehicle crawled for several more yards . . . and died.

"No!" she muttered. Refusing to accept their fate, she turned the key and pumped the pedal. A moment later the engine caught, and she breathed a relieved sigh as the car shot forward once more—until it choked and wheezed to a final halt.

She sat behind the wheel, numbed by their dire predicament. Without the breeze generated by the four-wheeler's movement, its interi-

or would soon turn into an oven. She hit the steering wheel with her fist. If she survived this ordeal, she was moving back to New York City! No more desert for her. The hottest thing she would face again would be a photographer's lights.

But, of course, that wasn't true. She couldn't do that to Davey. She couldn't uproot him, couldn't subject him again to conditions that aggravated his asthma, couldn't leave him for days at a time while she went out on foreign locations.

Dear God, would she ever see her son again? And Cade? But what difference would that make? Someday he would leave. Nothing was permanent. Hadn't her mother's death—Mario's death—taught her that much? Oh, why hadn't she tried to appreciate the precious time she and Cade had shared together rather than demanding eternity or nothing?

Perspiration, her body's vital liquid, trickled off her face as she got out and once more grappled with Robles's inert body. After tugging him from the back seat, she pulled him around to the lee of the car, where the sun's blistering fingers couldn't reach. She propped herself against one large tire, then checked her watch. Not yet one o'clock. The hottest part of the day was still to come.

She fanned herself with her hat, but even that negligible motion seemed to drain her energy. Better to conserve it for possible future need. How long before Hernandez realized that she was missing? Would he guess where she had gone? Overhead, shadowy vultures, their death's wings widely spread, swooped on unseen air currents.

Too soon the body's natural cooling system would cease to function. With the loss of water, cramping in the arms, legs and stomach would begin. Then the temperature would soar and the tongue would start to swell. Convulsions would follow. And after that . . .

Finding water was imperative. But where on that burning desert could she find it? Her eyes swept the barren vista. Not even a cactus to cut open for its juice. In the heat her brain was subsiding into a comfortable lethargy. Logic told her that she had to do something immediately, before her body ceased to act on her brain's signals.

But do what?

Next to her Robles, sprawled face upward, babbled incoherently. She stood up and concentrated on her surroundings. Then she laughed, laughter that was too close to hysteria. The car—the very thing she leaned on—it contained water of some sort! She scrambled to her feet, ran around to the front and lifted the hood. Just that small exertion made her dizzy. She braced herself on the car's grill, and the metal scorched her palms.

Carefully she looked over the engine's components. The radiator! She knew that the water in it was mixed with a coolant, but she didn't know just how poisonous the chemical might be. She had heard of a man drinking a bottle of aftershave to survive in the desert, but who knew what was in that radiator?

Her gaze jumped to the clear plastic object at the back of the engine compartment. The windshield washer reservoir. Of course! She never bothered to put antifreeze in the water, so it was completely safe to swallow. Within seconds she loosened the hose running to the reservoir and unsnapped the plastic container from its shelf.

Despair shriveled her soul when she saw how little water was in the container—barely more than a cup. The precious liquid was warm, stale and had a metallic flavor, but she didn't believe that even a glass of lemonade would have tasted nearly as delicious at that moment. She closed her eyes, savoring the pure ecstasy of the water on her tongue.

She rationed herself to what she judged was a couple of ounces. With so little water, and Robles still needing his share, it would be wise to conserve as much as possible—especially since the two of them still had to face the hottest part of the day. As if she were holding a hand grenade, she carefully carried the reservoir back to Robles. When she tilted its rim to his cracked lips, more water ran out the corners of his mouth than down his throat.

No perspiration sheened his skin. With his high body heat, convulsions would soon set in if she didn't get him to swallow more water. And what would happen to both of them after their water source was depleted?

She tried again, and this time it seemed as if he swallowed a little more. Exhausted by such a small effort, she sank down onto the sand beside him. An eerie silence lay over the desert, only to be broken by Robles's sudden delirious ravings. When his thrashing hand knocked over the reservoir she cried out as the spilt water seeped into the sand. She could have wept.

After that, apathy settled over her. To attempt to leave the car would invite certain disaster. She settled back against the wheel to wait. Her growing drowsiness seemed a welcome respite from the unbearable heat. But an insect's droning interfered. Eyes closed, she waved her hand distractedly before her. Yet the whirring continued, amplifying like some giant-winged beast. She knew now that she, too, was growing delirious with the heat.

Cassie caught Hernandez's head between her hands and planted a kiss on its shiny dome. "You marvelous man! Your Juanita is a lucky woman."

Like Snow White's bashful dwarf, he dipped his head and grinned. His scuffed boot polished the clinic's immaculate tile. "I was just doing my duty, *señora*."

"If you hadn't contacted the Border Patrol, Robles and I would be food for the vultures by now. I never thought I'd be so glad to see a helicopter."

"The Reinharts—they will not be so glad, eh?"

With a perfunctory smile she took the holster the nurse behind the counter passed her and began to buckle it about her waist. "After I fill out the release form, Hernandez, the next form I sign will be an offense complaint against Eric. The Reinharts can't continue to get away with this vigilantism."

The Mexican handed her Stetson to her. "Your duck will be cooked, *señora*," he warned.

She smiled despite the gloomy prediction. "My goose will be cooked, you mean. And the Reinharts started heating the oven for roast goose when I went after Robles. So I might as well see this thing through."

Her light-hearted words belied her anxiety. What chance did she stand against the influence and power wielded by the Reinharts? She really was a fool. She had not only sacrificed her job but her own and Davey's future happiness—all for outdated concepts of right and justice. Abstractions. They counted for nothing when one wondered where one's next dinner was coming from.

Once the doctor certified that she was in good health and could be released, she left Hernandez to take the office calls for the remainder of the afternoon and, after picking up Davey, went straight home. She felt like a malfunctioning computer that was on "down time."

A telephone call from Marilyn interrupted the seclusion she had sought. "I heard you were in the clinic today," her friend said breathlessly. "The word is out that you were lost in the desert with Robles. Are you all right?"

"I'm fine, but Robles is being held overnight for observation."

"Good golly, Cassie, if you were going to get lost in the desert with a man, why didn't you do it with someone like Cade?"

"That would be hard to do, since he's left town," she said flippantly, though her heart felt like it would crumple into her boots.

"For good?" Marilyn piped.

She sighed. It would be wonderful to get in bed and pull the covers over her head. "I don't know. Hernandez only told me a little while ago that Cade left town yesterday—something about flying to New York to coordinate the longshoremen's boycott against Reinhart chiles."

"Curly says that Reinhart Farms is suffering under the strike, so it can't be too much longer before the old man is forced to negotiate a contract."

If Cassie had felt bad when she learned that Cade had deserted her, she found out that she could feel even worse when she read the paper the next week. She knew that she would soon experience the misery of mass defection after reading a *Lordsburg Independent* editorial against her candidacy, citing her "impropriety in cohabitating with a man."

"Is this the kind of moral behavior Lordsburg citizens want in their elected officials?" the article asked. It finished by advocating a vote for the other write-in candidate—Roberto Manuel Rico.

"Rico!" she cried and wadded up the newspaper, flinging it at the metal wastebasket and missing. "He wouldn't know his nostrils from the end of a double-barreled shotgun!"

Hernandez chortled and collected the missed shot from the floor to drop it in the wastebasket. "If Rico wins, we all go to Mexico, eh?"

She would have to go somewhere after the election was over. If the turned backs she faced on Lordsburg's streets over the following days were any indication, she and Davey would be about as welcome there as a nuclear plant. Only a few friends, like Marilyn and Curly and Anaberta, remained loyal during those last few days before the election. Others, like old man Haskell, Percy Duncan and Hiram Blake, rode the fence, which was in effect a vote against her.

When she went to the Reinhart offices to serve papers on Eric, his grin was openly derisive. "I'll have you crawling to me, Widow Woman, before this ever comes to trial."

"The desert will ice over first," she snapped, and slammed the door as she stalked from his office. But her heart was frozen with fear. She felt besieged on all sides. She was alone with no one to turn to, the proverbial pariah.

That night Cade called. The static on the line told her it was long distance. "Cass," he said in that rough-timbred voice of his.

"Yes?" It was as if a vacuum had sucked all the oxygen from the room, making speech almost impossible.

"Armadeo just told me about your close call at Hell's Furnace. Are you all right?"

"Yes?" Was that all she could say—yes? Why didn't she tell him that she loved him, that she wanted him with or without a binding commitment. She just wanted him.

A long pause ensued, then, "How's Davey?"

"Fine. The duck's laying eggs, but Davey still persists in calling it Donald. We have another mare about to foal." She knew she was talking inanely, but she couldn't stop her insipid babble. "How are the contract negotiations going with Reinhart's lawyers?"

"Fine," he echoed. "Our lawyers here feel a settlement is imminent."

She gulped back the words of love that trembled on her lips. "And the novel?" she asked instead. "Is it coming along fine, too?"

"Fine." The one word was spoken tersely.

Didn't either of them know how to carry on a conversation using words other than "yes" and "fine"? Apparently not, for she could think of nothing else to say . . . and she wanted to say so much. "Well . . . goodbye, Cade."

"Goodbye, Cass—Widow Woman."

Chapter 15

THE WEEK BEFORE THE ELECTION, THE
Lordsburg Independent announced the contract settlement between the HCFWA and
Reinhart Farms. Cade had broken the Reinharts' power over the farm workers.

As they did during the spring chile festival,
the streets filled with laborers rejoicing in the
settlement. Armadeo, whom the paper reported was the newly appointed head of HCFWA,
was besieged by state reporters. Even Hernandez was jubilant, because he was leaving
that weekend to finally bring his Fatima back
to Lordsburg. Everyone was happy. Everyone
but the Reinharts—and Cassie.

Once the celebration was over things settled
down again to the peaceful, sleepy way they

had been before Cade Montoya came to town. Or almost. She knew that the Reinharts would not be satisfied until they had exacted their revenge on her for her part in the strike that summer. They were determined that she would not be elected sheriff. And she knew that they still wielded enough influence in other areas to carry out their revenge. What would she do after she handed in her badge? The ranch would have to be sold; they would have to move. And after that? It didn't bear thinking about. Not then. She would worry about their future after the election.

Her father had been right—it hadn't been a peaceful summer. And her heart still knew no peace. During the lonely nights she restlessly wandered the house. She surprised herself by sometimes playing the piano, softly, so as not to wake Davey. The songs were sad ones, but at least she had returned to her music. Cade had given it meaning again for her. She had that much to thank him for.

The day before the election, Sunday, she dragged herself from bed. She knew that everyone would attend church that morning, hoping to see if their morally corrupt sheriff had the courage to show her face. All they probably lacked was a hangman's noose, she thought dismally as she dressed herself and Davey. He looked as glum as she felt. His morose expression had not altered since the day Cade left. Even Davey's duck went neglected those days.

"Hey," she teased, nudging her fingertips against the drooping corners of her son's mouth. "Smile, son. Your mouth looks just like Donald's bill when you stick out your lips that way."

Davey's effort to smile tugged at her heart, and she mentally cursed uncaring people like Cade and Eric. When she drove up before the church and saw the crowd of people filing through the doorway, she had second thoughts about attending services. If there were only herself to worry about, she would have refused to back down. But there was Davey to think about. She knew that Eric had been freed on bail almost immediately after she had served papers on him. What if he made a cutting remark in front of Davey?

Despite her forebodings, she entered the church. Noses tilted upward and heads turned away as she and Davey found seats in a middle pew. She felt like Daniel in the lions' den. With Marilyn and Curly absent that morning, the people who filled the pews could only be considered her adversaries, since none of them had the courage to defy the Reinharts.

Her hopes of escaping the church unscathed were dashed when she saw Eric and his father sitting only several pews away from Miss Creighburg. She doubted if the Reinharts and Miss Creighburg would overlook the opportunity to taunt her before the congregation.

They didn't. After the services, as she made her way to the car, Jonathan Reinhart's imperious voice thundered over the small groups of people gathered in the churchyard. "Widow Woman!"

Slowly she turned, trying not to squeeze Davey's hand as bitterness and anger welled inside her. The parishioners made way for Jonathan and Eric Reinhart as the two men bore down on her. They halted a couple of yards short of her, far enough away to justify raising their voices. Jonathan Reinhart's head jutted forward. "As a concerned citizen of our community, Mrs. Garolini, I'm sure I represent my fellow church members in demanding the removal of your name from tomorrow's election ballot."

His ruthless eyes raked the mute congregation, as if daring them to refute his statement. Beneath his glare, their heads ducked in what could only be interpreted as acquiescence to the influence he wielded. She couldn't blame them. They had their own jobs to defend, their families to feed. Looking around her, she saw in many faces sympathy for her plight. But their sympathy would not protect her now.

From the steps the minister cleared his throat. "Er, Mr. Reinhart, this is not the place to conduct politics."

But his words fell ineffectually on the older Reinhart's ears. "Well?" the grower demanded of her. "Will you withdraw your name, or do we have—"

"Mama," Davey interrupted, tugging at her hand. "What's the man talking about?"

She wanted to cry—more for her son than herself. With the Reinharts all but uniting the citizens against her, she saw no alternative but to accede to their demand. At that point she wasn't even certain that she really cared about the election. She was already defeated in spirit by Cade's desertion.

"All right," she told Jonathan Reinhart wearily. "I'll—"

"She'll remain on the ballot tomorrow."

All heads swiveled toward the direction of the voice. One arm braced against the giant cottonwood, Cade surveyed the congregation coolly before he straightened and strode toward Cassie and Davey. The parishioners parted ahead of him as though he were Moses dividing the Red Sea. When Davey realized who was coming toward him, he cried out, "Cade!" and ran to throw his arms about the man's legs.

Anchored by the boy's hold, Cade halted in mid-stride. Across the intervening distance his eyes met Cassie's. Almost every adult in the churchyard felt the impact of the sizzling message in his gaze. But his words were directed to Jonathan Reinhart. "You were charging her with immorality, I believe, Reinhart?"

"Fornication!" Miss Creighburg said, shaking her cane at Cade. "Living in sin with you, she was!"

"You have your answer," the older Reinhart told Cade and brushed his palms together, like Pilate washing his hands of guilt.

Eric smiled triumphantly. "The Widow Woman can't fight public opinion, Montoya."

Cade ruffled Davey's hair affectionately. "She doesn't need to," he said laconically. He released Cassie from his gaze and swept his eyes over the people with calculated deliberation. With almost baited breath they waited to hear the conclusion to the challenging statement.

"The Widow Woman is going to be my wife."

The joggers kicked up little puffs of dust on the caliche road that intersected the two-lane highway. Between them loped a large dog that was a cross between a coyote and a German Shepherd. The couple halted on either side of the mailbox. The man, looking massive and powerful in his jogging shorts, withdrew one particular envelope from among the cluster of advertisements, circulars and mail-order catalogues. He flicked the young woman's chin with the envelope in a teasing gesture, saying, "My first advance check on *The Earth's Song*."

The young woman tossed her mane of summer-white hair in mock disdain. "That makes me a kept woman, I suppose?"

"As of yesterday—no. Lordsburg's newly elected sheriff is now properly married."

"Oh, very married, Mr. McPherson."

Cassie stood on her tiptoes and leaned over the mailbox. Her hands splayed on Cade's chest, which was damp with perspiration despite that the fact it was already the first week in November. "I would say a quick wedding ceremony in Juarez yesterday followed by a very long night in your bed makes me most certainly married. Hmmm, Cade," she said, nuzzling her lips against his jaw, "I think I like it when you don't shave every day."

"You're overheating my body temperature," he warned. Then, "Cassie, when Armadeo told me about your close call at Hell's Furnace, I knew my wandering days were over. I knew before then, but I didn't want to admit it to myself."

Her fingertip dammed a rivulet of sweat that had run into the pit grooved in his chin. "When did you first realize it?" she asked with the coquettishness of a woman who knows she's loved.

"Remember the night of the storm?" His teeth playfully nipped at her finger. "It wasn't until later, in New York, that I realized I had left a very important meeting on the strike effort that night—something to which I had thought I was wholly committed. I had left it to see if you were all right." His voice grew husky. "Without your love, Cassie, nothing else is important to me. If you hadn't agreed to marry me, I would have—"

"—have done what?" she demanded with one of her provoking smiles.

He joined in her banter. "I would have locked you in the county jail with me and thrown away the key."

"You're just smoothing my ruffled feminine vanity because I let you leave your heroine Cate in the novel."

"I mean it," he protested, but his hazel eyes glittered with laughter. "If you hadn't married me, Miss Creighburg would never have let me live in peace at the ranch here. I would have had no choice but the jail—just think, I'd still have free meals, a bed and you."

"Cade," she said, hesitating, ". . . perhaps there's somewhere else you'd want to live?"

His lips arced in his gentle, lopsided smile. "I told you. I'm finished wandering, Cass. For sure. You're still the sheriff here, and you like your job—and I can write my novels anywhere. So Lordsburg is just fine with me . . . as long as I have you and Davey."

She leaned over the mailbox again to move her lips lightly over his. "With a ranch, a ready-made family and a new book in the works," she murmured in a low, sensuously teasing voice, "what more could you want?"

"You," he growled. "Right here on the pavement."

At their feet Pee Wee echoed the growl when Cade's hands captured her shoulders and pulled her as close to him as the mailbox would permit. His mouth closed over hers in a deep, thorough kiss that told her of his abiding love.

The envelopes he had held fluttered to the ground, only to be scattered along the highway as a truck roared by, buffeting the two people with wind. The diesel's horn blew in a salute to the embracing couple.

When Cade released her, she said breathlessly, "I think we had better wait to finish what we started until we get back home."

"Home . . . I like the word, Cass. And I love you. For sure."

If you enjoyed this book...

Thrill to 4 more Silhouette Intimate Moments novels (a $9.00 value)— ABSOLUTELY FREE!

If you want more passionate sensual romance, then Silhouette Intimate Moments novels are for you!

In every 256-page book, you'll find romance that's electrifying...involving... and intense. And now, these larger-than-life romances can come into your home every month!

4 FREE books as your introduction.

Act now and we'll send you four thrilling Silhouette Intimate Moments novels. They're our gift to introduce you to our convenient home subscription service. Every month, we'll send you four new Silhouette Intimate Moments books. Look them over for 15 days. If you keep them, pay just $9.00 for all four. Or return them at no charge.

We'll mail your books to you *as soon as they are published.* Plus, with every shipment, you'll receive the Silhouette Books Newsletter absolutely free. *And Silhouette Intimate Moments is delivered free.*

Mail the coupon today and start receiving Silhouette Intimate Moments. Romance novels for women...not girls.

Silhouette Intimate Moments

Silhouette
Intimate 🖤 *Moments*

more romance, more excitement

———— **$2.25 each** ————

Silhouette
Intimate 💕 *Moments*

more romance, more excitement

Silhouette Intimate Moments

Coming Next Month

Morning Star by Kristen James

Country and Western star C.J. Casey was the man Cathleen blamed for her father's downfall, yet he was the only man who could call forth the music in her soul and the love in her heart. Though the world fell away when they sang together, could she forget the past and surrender to his love?

Crystal Blue Desire by Monica Barrie

Kat could guide her yacht safely past the most perilous reef, but now she was in danger of losing her heart. Bayliss Granger affected her like no man she'd ever known, but he knew more about the past Kat had left behind than she suspected.

Wind Whispers by Barbara Faith

Joanna Morrow and Carlos Quintana met to work on a mural celebrating Mexico's past. As they painted the ancient legend of two lovers, their own love began to overwhelm them. Could they challenge the legacy of the sad legend and remain together for all time?

Cry for the Moon by Pamela Wallace

Revel Tyson was determined to save the airline that bore her family name. Connor Winfield was just as determined that her planes would fly as part of his fleet. But neither was ready for the passion that crackled between them and made things suddenly more complicated than they expected.